Grand

Grand

Becoming my
mother's daughter

Noelle McCarthy

PENGUIN BOOKS

PENGUIN

UK | USA | Canada | Ireland | Australia
India | New Zealand | South Africa | China

Penguin is an imprint of the Penguin Random House group of companies,
whose addresses can be found at global.penguinrandomhouse.com.

Penguin
Random House
New Zealand

First published by Penguin Random House New Zealand, 2022

1 2 3 4 5 6 7 8 9 10

Text © Noelle McCarthy, 2022

The moral right of the author has been asserted.

Design by Katrina Duncan © Penguin Random House New Zealand
Cover photograph © Stephen Langdon
Author photograph by Rebecca Zephyr Thomas
Prepress by Image Centre Group
Printed and bound in Australia by Griffin Press, an Accredited
ISO AS/NZS 14001 Environmental Management Systems Printer

A catalogue record for this book is available from
the National Library of New Zealand.

ISBN 978-0-14-377610-9
ISBN 978-0-14-377831-8 (audio)
eISBN 978-0-14-377611-6

penguin.co.nz

For my sister, Sarah

One

When I was very small I loved wolves, she told me. I used to go to bed with one under my pillow, couldn't fall asleep without him. The wolf in Eve's Little Red Riding Hood book has a big bushy tail and a tweed jacket with a knife and fork in his top pocket. All the better to eat you with, Madam. We got a different version of the story out of the library recently, a beautifully illustrated one where nobody rescues Red Riding Hood at the end, she stays in the wolf's belly. Eve took it in her stride, but I was haunted.

Mammy was a werewolf, it only took one sip of drink to change her. The first mouthful of the first pint of Carling, all the evil came out dancing. Her face would change, but subtly; her eyes would brighten and her nose would lengthen. Everything about her became wilder and sharper and more alert. That was when the barman would need to watch himself.

It took some of them a while to realise it. Like the place she got thrown out of on Blarney Street for screaming that her glass was dirty. The miracle was, she never ran out of bars, or taxi drivers, even as she ate up every one who crossed her. They'd reach their limit sometimes, call in reinforcements, rattled by her savagery. She'd sit in the front seat, us in the back in our school uniforms, parked up outside the Guards station, a glass of bright green in her hand still, like we were at a cocktail party. Vodka and a dash of lime cordial. Even the Guards didn't know what to do with her; a grandiose drunk baiting her taxi driver, refusing to pay him because he wasn't deferential enough, insulted her somehow, her children in the back seat, on a Tuesday. The Sergeant would just tell the driver to take us home, ask my father for some money.

She wrote me a card one year. It has a wolf on the front of it, lapping at a silver pool of water, a big moon behind him glowing. That overwrought, romanticised kind of animal portraiture you see on jigsaws, velour blankets and heavy metal t-shirts. She got it in a little hole-in-the-wall she went to on the Coal Quay, a tiny place in one of the old workers' cottages, full of crystals and candles and similar. My Fairy Shop, she called it.

'Look at the wolf,' she wrote in my card, repeating what the witchy owner told her. 'He's looking into the water, seeing everything in it. He's aware of his surroundings. He's alone, but he can see himself in the water. He keeps himself company. Wolves are strong, brave and clever.' She wrote all this out carefully on a lined sheet of copybook paper and signed it 'Your crazy Momma, Caroline'. There's a lipstick kiss near the signature but I don't remember if she did that or I did.

I carry the letter around with me, folded up six times into a square in my wallet, wrapped around a small photo of my mother. It's a passport photo, black and white. She is very beautiful – dark eyes in a pale oval face, long dark straight hair parted in the centre falling well past her shoulders, very '60s, early '70s. She's wearing some sort of woolly jumper – white,

8

or pink maybe, with a high collar and a thin ribbon tied in a bow around the neckline. She's not smiling, but she looks completely relaxed, her brow unclouded. You can see her top teeth, her lips are parted, she's breathing easily. I could stare at this photo for hours, days maybe – as though by looking hard enough, I could somehow see in this perfect, silent teenager any trace of the woman who gave birth to me. See how she became the person she became later, the woman in the front seat of a Lee Cabs taxi outside the Guards station, with a vodka and lime in her hand and a bellyful of fury. I stare and I stare, and she stares back, the oval-faced girl with the ribbon on her jumper, who looks a little bit like Sharon Tate, with her poker-straight hair and general air of innocent sexuality. 'This was my girlfriend from 1969–1971,' someone has written on the back in pencil, faded but legible. She'd have been 16 years old in 1969. She met my father when she was 14, she always told me. That is not my father's writing on the back of the photo. He may have been her first boyfriend, but he wasn't her only one. I used to look at that photo sometimes and think about asking her who wrote it. But I never had the nerve to. I don't even remember how I got it – I have a habit of taking things when I am home on holiday, just squirrelling them away, not even asking for permission.

When I was a teenager, I sometimes used to wait until she was in bed, getting ready to go to sleep, and I'd run into the room and flash her a picture from one of my film magazines. A two-page spread from *An American Werewolf in London*. The moment of hairy transformation – man becoming wolf, the snout bursting through his nostrils, teeth elongating.

'Ah stop Noelle, stop it, you'll go to hell for that! Don't come near me with that – it freaks me!' she'd shriek, horrified and delighted, hiding under the blanket. 'Go away with it! May God forgive you.'

In my memory she is often in my bedroom on those nights. That may be because I'm older by then, and I'd already left it. Some nights, I climb into the bed beside her, feel the heat of her bare legs wrapped around me. She had very little hair anywhere on her body, her legs were never stubbly. I lie with her in the mother-den beneath the covers.

'They just don't stop, you know? Like, I don't know, were-wolves or something. They're all fucking crazy once they get the drink in them. Don't go to bed like normal people.' My dad on the phone, many years later, telling me about a night down in Kerry with my mother and her brothers and sister. I was like that too, obviously. The worst thing was not knowing how it would go on any given night. Would it be two drinks, then home, blameless? Or home two days later, minus a handbag, having spat at a stranger? I had no reliable indicator. It was the same for Carol. Two pints some days, and Daddy picking us up outside the funeral home, no drama. Other days, parked outside the Guards six hours later.

I never noticed at the time, what the moon was doing, but even now, many years since my last drink, at certain times of the month, I can feel the imp within me, an antic demon behind my teeth, using my mouth to make trouble. I want to get barred from places, I want to scream the glass isn't clean enough. I want to break things. There's a little police station up by the SuperValue. Some nights I want to be driven into it.

Two

The doctor's name is Byrne. A consultant oncologist. She'll have appreciated his air of authority, the undeniable doctorliness of him, even as she plotted to outwit him.

'Your mother is a lovely woman.' Slight trace of a Dublin accent in his voice down the phone to me, the only sound in a quiet house after midnight, last Monday night in New Zealand. 'A lovely person, but she didn't want the treatment. And of course that is her right,' he adds quickly.

I almost feel sorry for him. He's come up against her with no warning. 'She's a lovely person, and an intensely private person, and she's spent the last two or three months not letting anybody in.'

It's a sort of relief hearing that, finally, and from a medical professional. Try living with her, I want to say. Try being her daughter. 'The progression of her cancer is significant. Her blood sugars are out of control now there's no food going in.

With her diabetes, the underlying systems won't cope with this, ultimately.'

I write 'underlying' and 'ultimately' in the exercise book in front of me like a good journalist, marvelling in a detached kind of way – how often do you see two words beginning with u in the same sentence? No radiation – I can't say I blame her – and only two half-hearted goes at chemo. Can't blame her for that either, she wasn't more than six stone to begin with.

'What would you do if it was your mother?' The room is cold and the overhead light is in my eyes. I'm shivering.

'If it was me, I'd come home in the next day or two.' I almost laugh, it sounds so serious.

'How long do you think . . . ?'

'Within the next week I'd say, possibly two. I'd be getting on a plane right now, if it was my mother.'

But it isn't his mother. And now it's Thursday night, ten days later, and Sarah and I and Dr Byrne are all leaning awkwardly against a wall-mounted whiteboard in an empty corridor of an overheated women's ward in the Mercy. That's what everyone calls it here, not even hospital, just the Mercy.

He'd said a week, maybe two. But that was nearly ten days ago and now I'm here for a funeral, and she's still not dead, and I have my own daughter to go home to.

'So, in terms of time . . . ?' Awkward, trying to word it.

'Yes, well, in this sort of situation . . . where she's not eating, or drinking anything, you'd almost want to be able to put people out of their misery.' I feel Sarah stiffen beside me. He's looking at her the whole time, full-on eye contact, even though I'm the one asking the questions. His skin is smooth and rosy, more like a boy than a man. No white coat, but a fine wool suit, the mobile in his pocket buzzing constantly. 'Not that that's what should ever happen,' he adds hurriedly. 'Another few days, I think, if that even.' Is it my bright red coat, the red lipstick, that's making him not look at me? I always want to stand out when I'm back home, and then I'm ashamed when I do. 'She's not really open to hospice, is she? It's just, it would be a much better environment for her, at this stage.'

'She wants to go home, she thinks she's going home.' Sarah is nervous, but being firm with him, defending Mammy. I look down at her shoes, flimsy slip-ons, and feel a surge of irritation. They're paper thin, way too cold for this weather. She's always hated wearing shoes – Eve's the same, I've noticed recently. I am waiting for the person to materialise who knows how to handle all of this, knows all the right things to ask, but it's just the two of us here, nobody else is coming. I belt my coat tighter, even though I'm sweating.

'I'm so sorry, I know this is a very difficult time for all of ye.' Still a cliché, but at least it sounds sincere in the Dublin accent. She'll be enjoying that he's from there, she always made it sound glamorous being born in Drimnagh. Like it was Paris. 'I'll see about getting her her own room. The wards are so full . . . it's hard to manage.' He spreads his hands out in front of us, clean pink palms facing upwards in a gesture of helplessness. 'That's what we spend most of our time doing here, really, moving people.'

We murmur our thanks, wanting to be good, and grateful, conscious that Mammy is, once again, fucking someone's shit up. His suit is not the grey I took it for, but a soft, heathery purple. The light, fine wool glows against his cheeks and finally, I am as comforted by him as he wishes me to be, by the cleanness of him, his decent efficiency.

Earlier, I followed Sarah down the corridor of the hospital. Yellow walls, yellow floors, yellow fluorescent lights above us. It was stiflingly hot inside, after the freezing slap of the February night when we got out of the airport. The hospital smell is something fleshy covered up with disinfectant. Boiled food and the iron tang of blood beneath it. She's in a bed by the door, curled up like a small child in a fluffy pink dressing gown, one twig arm hooked up to clear tubes that snake along the bed beside her. My first thought: this is death. My second thought: she looks like Samuel Beckett. Her nose, always prominent, is massive, now that her cheeks have fallen in around it. I go up to the head of the cot, although I am frightened by the sight of her.

'Hello, tiny one.'

I talk to her like you would to a newborn, a helpless creature. She opens her eyes and they fill with tears. I don't know if it's the sight of me or just general misery. We sit her up and Sarah gives her what looks like a giant cotton bud. She dips it in a beaker of orange juice and moistens her mouth. Her top teeth are gone; the plate fell out after the chemo, my sister tells me later. I'm shocked at the unravelling of her; it's like being in a car that's suddenly travelling at 150. She doesn't say much to me.

She's agitated now; twitching the bedcovers, trying to neaten the stuff on top of her locker. Sarah fusses around the bed, tidying up tissues, topping up water. After two solid weeks of caretaking, this is her territory. John Paul and Robert come every night, she says, but you can tell she's in charge of everything. I sit in the chair by the bed, try to pull my addled self into the present. The Irish night is black against the window at the end of the room, beneath the television. There's a programme on with a studio audience, people in spangled dancing outfits. My brain is back in Dubai, where I left it. I take off my coat and wad it around myself, making a little nest to sink into.

'Where did you come from?' She's lying on her side, one hazel eye fixed on me keenly. She still has all her senses, whatever they're giving her.

'London.'

'You're very late in.'

'I had to wait for a connection.'

'Sarah will take you home now.' I've been here all of ten minutes. 'Go on, let ye. I want to go to sleep.'

We leave her, a tiny S shape under a velour blanket.

The next day, for want of anything better to do, I go to the funeral home. The director is a big man with an expensive black wool coat and a full head of suspiciously dark hair combed back off his forehead. He nods when I tell him my mother's name. 'We've looked after a number of the family here,' he says, like they're Kennedys. Another Cork-is-the-centre-of-the-universe person. I have a sudden memory of Mammy making me kiss a waxen Granda Bob in the room across from where we are sitting, the room with all the coffins in it. No memory of Nana being in there, which is for the best, really.

The director lays a blank sheet of paper on the desk and touches the top of it delicately. His nails are spotless, and slightly too long. I think of Count Dracula, putting contracts in front of Jonathan Harker.

'First thing now: the Notice.' Apparently, a death notice has to go in the local paper before anything else can happen. This being Cork, nobody wants to miss anything.

'So we are thinking . . . a few days . . . ?' He steeples his fingers together and trails off delicately. His tie is navy, with snow-white polka dots, bright but proper.

'Days, the doctor said last night, definitely.'

'OK. Today is Friday, tomorrow is Saturday, obviously, we do nothing Sunday. And the following Tuesday is out also, I can tell you that right now. There'll be no funerals in the diocese next

Tuesday, the clergy is meeting above with the Bishop.' He says this like I should be pleased for them. I'm trying to do the mental arithmetic, working back from my flight home in ten days' time. Rosary, removal, a day for the funeral.

The ideal scenario, I gather, is for Mammy to die some evening before the 8pm deadline of the local paper. That would allow the Rosary to be said the following evening. 'There is no extra charge to have the Rosary on one day, and the removal the next morning,' he tells me magnanimously. How many will come to the funeral, I wonder. Old friends from The Chimes, Chapel Hill, her nursing days? I've seen the little loudspeakers outside the funeral home, tucked under the awning. They pump the Hail Marys out to those gathered on the footpath at big removals. I'd have thought Mammy's disposition would have precluded big numbers, but you never know. Sarah maintains she was kind to people.

A red light flashes on the phone in front of us. The funeral director picks it up, listens. Puts it down, picks it up again, jabs a button. 'Denis, the lady from Redemption Road, is she in there?' Listens. Puts it down, picks it up again, the voice low and solemn: 'Yes, Mum is actually with us now. We'll see you after three today for the viewing.' He hangs up and looks back at me. 'Drop in her clothes at some stage. Doesn't matter if they're too big, we'll sort that out. Clothes only, no shoes, she won't need them.' Well, obviously, I stifle a giggle.

'Lipstick as well, if she wears it.' Rimmel, Heather Shimmer. I see her now, in the snugs of the pubs, in the back of all the taxis, pushing her lips out, making an O shape. Quick swipe, no mirror. Frosted purple, it made her look mildly hypothermic. She never strayed from it.

'Address?'

'Mine? Er, no, sorry it's –'

'We NEVER put the house number in the paper,' he shouts at me suddenly. 'Only the *locality*.' Sarah explains later it's so people don't rob you while you're out at the funeral.

The death notice will cost 350 Euro and there's a free repeat after six months, so people can say some sort of prayer for her. I nod, pretending this makes sense to me. She bought her own grave a long time ago, out on a wooded hillside near Blarney. All I need to do is sign, and Cork Corporation will open it. He slides a form in front of me. I stare down at it for a moment, imagining the men with shovels standing ready for my mother. I look around for someone to tell me it's OK to do this, but there's no one to give permission. I sign my name, accept a charge of 80 Euro.

'Now the service' – he opens his hands and sweeps them across the desk, conjuring an altar. A big ugly Apple Watch beeps discreetly on one hairy wrist – Irish people are mad for them, he's probably counting steps like my sister. 'The church have clamped down hugely on non-hymns,' he says severely, 'but you may get away with something at the processional.'

'Er, no, traditional is fine.' Mammy has a horror of pop songs in churches, thinks it's common. She loves a good funeral, reciting longingly all the highlights from every one she goes to. 'They did The Lonesome Boatman on the clarinet, and the Montfort Choir were on the altar . . .' On enquiry, it seems everyone she wanted to sing at hers is dead already.

As the undertaker is walking me out, my head spinning with details of musical interludes and floral arrangements, I see my cousin's wife sitting by the door talking to the receptionist. There's a moment of mutual shock – what the fuck is she doing here? – and then Mammy's voice again, on the phone one Sunday not that long ago. 'Brennie's after picking out her coffin below in McAuliffes. She does the hair for the corpses, so she gets a free one.'

'Oh my God, has it come to this already?' Brennie's eyes are wide with horror.

'I'm just getting ready, for when it comes to it.' I stammer, my face flaming. By dinnertime, this will be all over the Northside. Mammy will die if my father's family finds out she is dying. Die of fury. Of pure rage at the thought of them knowing her business. I hear Byrne's soft voice in my head. 'An intensely private person.' Sarah will kill me.

When I get back to my sister's there's a jug of water on top of the toilet, for flushing, presumably. My Dad is a plumber. There's a proverb about this, doctors' kids going barefoot or something? My brother and his wife are over from London, we're all staying in my sister's tiny inner-city cottage. This morning the water heater was pluming smoke out into the back garden. I text my Dad about the toilet and scrub the shower, weirdly soothed by the fake lemon smell of the Jif and the scald of water on my knuckles. Sarah texts from the hospital: No change. I can come over this evening if I want to. I'll go to West Cork in a couple of days, I decide, if there's nothing happening. I've only just got here and already the itch to get out is all over my skin. I'm jetlagged to fuck, I just want to sleep and walk up a hill.

Three

I am looking up at the kitchen clock high on the wall on the right-hand corner. It is a flat gold circle with spiky black numerals on every quarter: 3, 6, 9, 12. The hands are in between the 9 and the 12, so I know it's late. I have only learnt how to tell time recently. There's a priest sitting at the kitchen table, his back half-turned to me. I can see his face in profile, he looks as bewildered as I am to be in our kitchen not far off midnight. I'm sitting behind him and off to the right slightly, my back against the counter that runs parallel to our big window, separating the dining area from the rest of the kitchen. I'm sitting on a brown carpet, and the floor around me is sparkling with smashed pieces of a Carling Black Label bottle. They seem to be everywhere, maybe it's more than one bottle. I'm only aware of the priest and myself in the kitchen, but my mother or my father must have been around too, one of them must have called him. Our house is so new I can smell it; later on it'll smell like dog, and hot fat from the chip pan, and the Christmas trees she leaves up until February every year, but for now there's only the fresh smell of the wood and paint my father used to make the counter, and the clean synthetic smell of the plastic webbing at the carpet's edges.

We moved into Hollymount when I was a baby. My Dad, and two of my mother's brothers, and assorted friends, all tradesmen, worked together on two houses at the top of the Northside, where the city meets the country. A Housing Corporation scheme sold land cheap, or loaned young families the money to build houses. Ours were two of the first to go up: one for my mother and her family, the other for one of her brothers. 'We built privately,' Mammy would hiss at taxi drivers, breath sweet with drink as they drove us up from Shandon Street. She makes them take the Blarney Road wherever possible, avoiding the Corporation estates in Hollyhill, with their speed bumps on the road to foil the joyriders. But the priest must have come from Hollyhill Parish, it's the closest to us. I don't remember him saying anything, just both of us sitting in the kitchen. Me, watching the long shards of dark glass glittering in the thick new carpet; him saying nothing either; you could even hear the clock ticking regularly, which was scary. The priest shifts slightly in his chair, turning his back on me fully. He is looking at the back wall of the kitchen, where two African serving spoons hang over the table. They are made of dark wood, with handles in the shape of a lion and a zebra. Auntie Cay brought them back from a safari. The chairs are gleaming silver, the table has a cloth with flowers on it for our birthday parties. Mammy never fails to give us one – she must have done twenty years of parties between us. Everything is new and nice in that house, throughout my childhood, until it isn't.

The priest must have gone in the end, and someone makes me go to bed, but I don't remember. He has reddish hair, parted down the middle, longer than you'd think it would be, and thick black glasses, of the sort that are now quite fashionable. He wears his black dress, and his white collar. I don't know who summoned him. Maybe my Dad rang him? It's not like him, but he might have been at the end of his tether already. I can't be sure I didn't dream it. A lot of my childhood memories are like this, flashes that go off in my head sometimes, that come back to me with a force that knocks the breath out of my chest, sends me looking for a pen, or texting my brother, or my sister. Do you remember the priest, the taxi driver, the rabbit? Sometimes they do, and sometimes they remember something else entirely. Nobody remembers the priest but me, but that makes sense – I was very young, maybe 4, and I am the eldest. My brother and sister, would have been babies, if they'd been born even. That's the only priest I remember being in our house, except for one who came to stay once. He was a distant cousin I think, back from the missions. He was very holy and very skinny. Mammy caught me looking at him through the keyhole of the guest room door, 'Noelle, you'll go to hell, stop it.' He was getting changed after a shower, but all I got was a flash of thin flanks and bony shoulders. She was never as fond of priests as you'd think a devout Catholic would be. She pretends to be asleep when one comes to see her in the Mercy. 'Let him go 'way out of that, don't be annoying me,' she hisses to my sister in a whisper.

The priest stands out, because not many people came to our house, that I remember. Apart from cousins. One of my father's sisters had five daughters who lived not far away. The oldest ones must have been useful babysitters. There's photos of Mammy marching one of them, aged about 14, and her friend up and down the front room, making them stand on the marble

21

fireplace, hands on their hips, posing. A Miss World pageant, she told them. 'Shoulders back, big SMILE. Come on, ye want to win it, don't ye?' It must have been the swimsuit section, they're only wearing t-shirts and knickers. It was summer, my cousin's fair hair is bleached white in places, her legs beneath her red t-shirt are long and golden.

The only dinner party Mammy had, someone died before it started. One of my grandmother's sisters' husbands, I think it was. She had five sisters, my great aunts – I don't remember any of them. Mammy was making a steamed pudding, a recipe she venerated, passed down from her mother and reaching back through generations. I remember it as a kind of stew-horror, grey coloured, topped with suet dumplings. The lid on the pressure cooker was long lost (I used it to give the dog his dinner) so Mammy used an old tin lid, weighted down with a half a brick from the garden. The pot on the stove looked like something from a witch's kitchen, the stew hissing and seething beneath the masonry. The house was full of the smell of cooked meat and warm dripping when the first of the old people arrived, weeping. My grandmother Han was brought into the front room, where she lit innumerable cigarettes and directed the serving of sherry and madeira cake to sorrowing relatives. I watched prawn cocktails congealing in little cut glasses on the kitchen table, my mother had already put out the starters. She had a horror of mayonnaise that she passed on to me – I remember the prawns swimming in it.

Han comes to babysit me sometimes. If my parents are going out at night together, she's ferried up to Hollymount by my father from her house by the Cathedral. We had a dog by the time I was a year old, a glossy Irish setter called Sam who Mammy said was depressive. Late at night, she'll crouch down in front of him, where he lies in a gleaming red heap at the foot of the stairs, staring at him intently. 'Yeah, you're very low, boy, I know you are. God help us, I'll say a prayer for you.' Han is also a big fan of Sam's, she comes with a bag of Maltesers and a bottle of Schweppes lemonade in her handbag, both of which will be mixed together in a big bowl as soon as my parents are gone. She says Sam and I can share it. Han never lasts long in Hollymount, she insists my father come home and drive her back down the hill after a few hours. "Tis the altitude John, I'm not able for it.'

I can't remember when we start fighting properly. Figuring out how to get her removed from bars, I think, has a lot to do with it. Pubs are boring. Carmel glares as I fling my crisps on the floor, narrowing her kohl-rimmed eyes at me. 'She knows exactly what she's doing.' Eventually the barman starts saying no as soon as he sees them coming with the buggy. I am the least compliant of my siblings. They can sit my sister on a high stool and she'll polish the darts trophies. Mammy bribes me as best she can, packets of crisps, glasses of raspberry. She hates paying for Coke, she says – it's the unfairness of the mark-up more than anything. She'll give us money for the occasional slot machine or computer game, though, if the bar is an early adopter of technology. More often than not, the only thing in there to play with is a jukebox. Learning how to read the rows and rows of songs, bands, singers that grew more familiar into the 1980s. Sweet Caroline, Uptown Girl, Islands in the Stream. Neat writing first, replaced with thin slips of typed paper: 20 pence a song, six for a pound. She gets a pile of coins, sends me over the other side of the room, grabbing a few more minutes with Carmel and Philly. She must resent me furiously. But my father is out working, doing his plumbing jobs, there's no one else to mind me, not during the day, where would she say she was going?

The wallpaper in The Chimes is dark wine-coloured, with a bamboo print on it. They lift me up onto one of the banquettes and I pick away at the edges of the bamboo shoots until there are bald patches. The lounge smells of old pints and fresh cigarettes, the savoury stink of cheese-and-onion Taytos. Carmel and Philly are there, before us, or after us, the long white necks of their plastic bags of messages twining with Mammy's on the spongy carpet, spilling open their contents: sliced pans, boxes of marrowfat peas, bottles of diluted orange. The pints stand on Beamish barmats before them in a sparkling huddle. That's where they get Philly's son to do his party pieces, poems he learns at school, mainly. Philly is tiny, with one turned eye, fiercely loquacious. 'Ciúnas, le bhur dtoil!' She shouts in the Gaelic she sometimes switches to for special occasions. And the lounge falls silent. One year, Philly organises turkeys for everyone in The Chimes and then goes missing, so nobody has a Christmas dinner. She answers the phone at somewhere called the Cork Gay and Lesbian Helpline. Mammy always says 'She's very good in her own way'.

One day I come out of school and Mammy and Carmel are waiting in the back of a taxi. 'Get in 'til you see what we got you,' says Mammy. I sit in the front, like an adult. The car smells of drink and Estée Lauder – White Linen, or Aliage. Wherever they've been, they've been there all morning. Carmel has her long arms around a cardboard box that is shaking violently, trying to keep hold of whatever is inside it.

'You'll have to mind him, give him curly green cabbage.' Mammy taps the side of the box. It lifts a few centimetres up into the air, sides bulging. Carmel throws herself forward over it, Medusa curls flying, the ash from her fag all over the seat in front of her. I reach for the seat belt. It's way too long for me.

'Up past the Crucifixion, please.' Mammy sounds haughty. His knuckles are white on the steering wheel. They'd have kept him outside The Chimes a good half hour. There's loud scrabbling from the back, the witchy sound of long nails scraping. The statues blur past: dying Christ, his weeping mother.

'Father, Son and Holy Spirit. Come on, girl!' Mammy blesses herself, insists I do the same. The driver thumps his chest three times with a vengeance.

Passing the asylum, the box flies open. A savage kick, a flash of fur, thrilling and alien. Carmel tries to jam the flap back down. 'For fuck's sake, hold onto him!'

Mammy is high, triumphant. Children's Allowance day, maybe. I am deeply excited about whatever is in the box, even though it's Carmel holding it. Her son catches pigeons when we're outside The Chimes, just throws his jacket over them. I don't know what happens to them afterwards. She's trying to keep the box steady. Whatever's inside is trying to tunnel through the bottom.

Outside Hollymount, Mammy makes the driver wait for his money, counting out coppers. Her bag is all over the back seat, Silvermints and tissues, Granda's Mass card; she refuses to gather it up in any kind of hurry. She wants to provoke him, there's a perceived lack of deference in all of these encounters that infuriates her. She doesn't have a key but the side gate is open. Released from its box, the rabbit is enormous. Grey and mangy with massive hind legs, it quivers all over.

'A buck,' says Mammy approvingly. Crazed from the journey, it runs straight at the garden wall and finds a too-small hole to jam itself into. When I try to pull it out, it makes a thin wailing noise like a baby.

'Don't go into her, boy, she'd fucking eat you.' The next-door neighbour. Mammy hates her. One of her boys called her an alkie once when she took his ball off him. She puts Daddy's big metal toolbox under the window ledge and stands up on it.

Carmel stays by the washing line, smoking. Her black clip-on earrings have streams of crystals that reach down to her shoulders. 'You'd want to mind that rabbit your mother got you.' I turn my back on her.

'Christ's sake, help me Carmel, I don't want to knock the Busy Lizzie.' My mother is pushing against the glass like a cat, her fingers working the catch on the window. Last time, she cut her hand open. Blood all over her good blue dress, must have been a wedding they were at, or a christening. Carmel braces her leg and she pulls herself up and into the kitchen.

The rabbit is trying to dig its way under the fuchsia by the back wall, white cotton tail in the air, hind legs pumping furiously. There's room in the hutch after the guinea pigs got eaten but I'll have to catch it. I imagine Daddy coming in from work, Carmel sitting in the kitchen, the bottle with the blue label on the table in front of them. The next time I see the rabbit, he's on the main road, we left the side gate open. Mammy breaks ice cubes out of their tray. 'He'll come back, he's only exploring.'

Four

I'm five years old, in senior infants. I have an ugly brown-and-cream uniform and a yellow-and-blue school bag about the same size as me. I finish school at 1 o'clock and Len is waiting. Len is my mother's brother, the eldest of her six siblings. He is tall and thin with sharp eyes behind glasses, and a big nose, like my mother's. He has a full head of hair that he wears swept back off his face, first it is dark, and then later silver like my grandfather. He has never married and does outlandish things like run marathons. He is also, in a show of health consciousness that makes him a white rhino in my mother's family, a fanatical non-smoker. On his lapel he wears a little shiny pin of a cigarette twisted into a knot and a red X through it. He has a clear, loud voice and says 'Aha!' when he is surprised, or pleased, which is all the time. Enthusiasm is Len's defining quality. When I was born he was nearly 40. He takes me into town to the Capitol Cinema. In the booth at the front door is a small man with a comb-over, wearing a silky waistcoat and grubby red bowtie. He gives us two paper tickets, then rushes out of the booth and tears our tickets in half in front of the big red doors of the theatre.

The floor inside is black and sticky. The seats are rich blue velvet, with bald patches in places. They flip back up if I don't sit my whole bottom on them properly. The film is called *E.T.* My memories of it are a river of confused impressions 40 years later; E.T. beneath a sheet, going trick or treating, a little girl with white fluffy string in her pigtails, like my American cousin, a pot of yellow flowers that wilt and come back to life again at climactic moments. I sit beside Len in the dark, too shocked to cry when the wrinkled brown creature with the long neck and big bright eyes starts dying in front of us. Afterwards we walk outside and the world is different. Bikes can fly across the moon, creatures exist that are beyond my knowledge. I don't remember Len explaining who Steven Spielberg was, he simply talked about him like we both knew him. He maintained no distance from his heroes, the cinematic ones especially. Many years later, not long before I leave for New Zealand, my father takes me for lunch. Len, he says, was on to him earlier. 'A friend of his is after dying, fella called Kubrick, did you know him?'

I am about six years old when Mammy tells me about Tara and Jonathan, over a pint of Carling and a Coke for me, in the Left Bank Bar. The Left Bank is the first in a line of dubious hostelries and early houses along the quay. You descend rickety stairs and find yourself in the middle of a small dark room below street level, windowless and circular, like a smoke-stained submarine. It is one of Mammy's hideaways, she has nooks and crannies all over the city. Wherever we go, she tends to sit where she can watch the door, she hates being surprised by anyone while she's drinking.

A long bar curves around the back wall of the Left Bank, presided over by a frenetic woman from up the country. She makes great big heaping plates of ham sandwiches and throws them out at her drinkers, most of whom spend the day in there, emerging into the dank twilight with bellies full of Beamish, lighter pockets and yellow fingers.

'Feed the men! Feed the men! Sure you have to!' she yells at my mother, passing around the big metal platters, smiling at her in a misjudged pantomime of sisterly solidarity. Mammy tells us privately that Patsy is crazy. Manic is the term she uses. Mammy is an expert on this because of her psychiatric nursing training. But she is always pleasant enough to Patsy, until one day when she isn't and then the Left Bank is no longer an option. She has knife-edge relationships with several barkeeps around the city. These are purely transactional and prone to disaster: a misbehaving child, a mistimed request for two pint bottles of Carling to take away and I'll fix you up next week, Patsy. And then it's out the double doors with Carol and her buggy. But while the going is good, the Left Bank is a discreet and convenient location, just across the road from McAuliffes funeral home, where my father collects us after she gets her messages.

We are in town that day buying shoes for my First Holy Communion, white leather Clarks, the ones with a golden key embedded in the heel. I chose them myself – they have gold buckles, and scalloped edges around the ankle strap, and tiny little flower designs picked out in holes in the leather. Magic Steps they are called, they were expensive. I had to have my foot properly measured, the woman in the shoe shop laying my soles flat against the green wooden plank with different numbers painted on it at intervals. At the bar afterwards, Mammy carefully sets the box in its plastic bag down on its own chair next to us – 'A shoe on the table means a fight, be careful!' – lights a Major and tells me the story of the children she had before me.

I am either the eldest of four or the third of six, depending on whether you want the official history of our family or the secret one. Tara and Jonathan are my sister and brother. The girl may not be called Tara any more – she was adopted in Dublin. Jonathan died soon after he was born. He is buried in a graveyard in Blackrock, where the river Lee meets the sea in Cork City.

My mother had Tara and Jonathan before she was married, which makes them illegitimate. From the moment I hear about these children, I consider them an existential threat to our family.

The first child was the product of rape, Mammy says, and do I know what that word means? I pretend I do, so she won't explain it. But she goes ahead and spells it out anyway. 'Rape is when a man has sex with you when you don't want him to,' she says. She never minces her words about that stuff – she explained the facts of life when I asked, aged around four, using words like sperm and ovum.

It's the dead child who makes the strongest impression. 'He's in a pauper's grave, down in Blackrock,' she says, and that makes him even deader, somehow. My mother has spent all her life on the Northside of the city. Everything we do – school, town, relatives – we do along the narrow ribbon that runs from our house in Hollymount, at the top of the Blarney Road, all the way down here to the quay and the bridge on the northern channel of the river. Blackrock is on the Southside, an anathema. Such a foreign place for her to have buried her baby, miles away from anywhere familiar. That's the point, though: he is out there because he is a secret, like his sister.

Mammy had Jonathan in the mid to late '70s, maybe eighteen months before me. She never gives exact dates, I work all this out decades later. In my memory, that day in The Left Bank, she has a pint in front of her but seems quite sober. She never again talks to me about Jonathan or Tara unless she's been drinking heavily. It is hard to make sense of her when she is like that, even if I wanted to – which I don't, especially not when she is talking about these children. They are the ultimate taboo, I understood that viscerally. That the little boy is dead is comforting, at least that means he can't come back and ruin us. The girl is a different story. I am terrified of the idea of her being out there somewhere.

At the end of the conversation, she raises her glass to me. 'We'll drink to them now, to Tara and her brother Jonathan.' I lift my Coke glass to hers, cracking the ice in my mouth afterwards. I know this information is dangerous, that it must never come out in the open. I know I can never tell Daddy, for example. That's why I am so outraged on the very bad nights, later on, when I go to my bedroom and she stands at the bottom of the stairs and screams the names of her lost children like a black magic incantation. These might have been around the time of the birthdays, one in March, one in April. 'Come down here and listen to me, listen about your brother and your sister! Tara and Jonathan, God help us, ye have no idea what I went through for them!'

She will scream this at me and at my father (it's only later I realise he couldn't possibly not have known about their existence) and as time goes on, she will scream it at my brother and my sister. She does it to make maximum trouble, to demand our attention. Sober, these names are off limits, as much a forbidden topic for her as for the rest of us. Day to day, she is a mother of three, then four, children, married and decent. But there is nothing she would hold her tongue about when she is drinking.

That is something we have in common, I find out later. I don't know how old Sarah and John Paul are when she tells them – maybe she takes them to the Left Bank as well, it's as good a place as any. It wouldn't have been that long after she had them, ten years or so maybe. But it all happened before I was born, so it feels like ancient history. Mammy talks about them both less as she gets older. Robert never even knew about the little boy, until recently.

Five

We get the train to Killarney and a bus from there. I don't really know why she's brought me, except maybe she had to bring one of us. The cash Daddy gave her is wadded up inside the black handbag with the thin, worn strap, next to Granda's Mass card.

The B&B is on the edge of the town, just before the cross-roads, at the end of the narrow road back into the village. A big, detached pebble-dashed hulk with old-fashioned green window frames and a few broken seashells stuck over the front door as a nod to the location. 'Ocean Vista', it says, in swirly letters by the front gate, erroneously. You can see the tip of an upturned boat if you glance around the side of the house, but she tells me to stay still while she knocks. She's nervous about being let in, but the woman just nods and leads us up the stairs, past the picture of Holy Mary in her bevelled frame, the sweet golden light from the stained-glass panes in the front door washing over her. At the top of the stairs, the window is open, filling the landing with the faint damp smell of seaweed and some kind of chemical fertiliser from the fields next door.

The room has a small sink in one corner, a kettle on top of a table with a box of teabags, and a small carton of milk. It's when I see the Kerry milk, with its big red rose logo, that I realise with a thrill, we've really done it. Carol knows too, and she is excited, which worries me. But I have my own bed: there are two singles, covered in ancient country quilts, scratchy blankets underneath them, like in the caravans up at the other end of the village.

'We'll take yours off, you'll be grand, it's nearly summer still,' she says quickly, before I can complain about being allergic.

We are there for the Pattern. I don't know where she heard of it. Lehane's probably, or The White Sands. She is always seizing on bits of Kerry weirdness and trying to get involved somehow. This is just an old-fashioned procession, like a May Day or Corpus Christi, except out of season. They get a statue of the Virgin Mary and take it up to the Holy Well at the other edge of the village, up on a cliff above the ocean. The well is named for a local Saint – Dathalain or Doireann, that kind of thing. She is said to cure blindness now, with her blessed water, but really, she was one of the ones that was there long before the Church, in a Pagan incarnation. People here have always worshipped at that place – the Pattern is a proper ancient rite, just in a Church of Rome version. Villagers mentioned the Pattern to Carol when we were down on our holidays in the summer, and she got it into her head to come back for it. Even now, I marvel at her enterprise. This is a woman who has neither a bank card nor her own front door key. But she loves trains, and she loves Kerry.

What do we do, once we get there? Hamburgers are the only thing I remember. Hamburgers from the chipper in the village. They are delicious. Soft buns and tender meat, and only tomato sauce, none of the pickles or mustard I hate from McDonald's. The chipper is a golden beacon when the drinkers spill out into the soft summer night after the national anthem at The White Sands and Lehane's. The delicious strangeness of Kerry chips, in long white plastic trays that smell of good clean fat, and cheap, sweet tomato sauce, heaped high on the tray with little red plastic tridents stuck into them. You never got forks like that in Cork. Upstairs was an amusement arcade – ten penny games for one or two players, 'We didn't Start the Fire' blasting down the concrete steps from the jukebox while you waited for your chips in the darkness. This weekend, I am allowed as many burgers as I want. The first night, it is already dark as we make our way to Lehane's. I told her to fuck off when she told me to bring my cardigan, but I am glad of it. Summer is only a few weeks gone, but it is starting to get cold already.

'I might chance a piece of fish. They never give you enough vinegar on the chips,' she says, wrinkling her nose. In the end she gets nothing. We stand outside, Billy Joel burning and turning, while I eat my burger, and then cross over to Lehane's, she gripping my fingers like when I was small, me trying to slap her hand away from me. I am worried for a minute they won't let me in: when we get to the door, there is a big sign with 18 in red letters on the glass and no kids inside. But nobody says anything, so I just find us a table and some seats in the corner.

'This will all be ready, now, tomorrow. They'll all be getting ready tonight, for The Pattern,' she says solemnly, putting her pint down carefully, lighting a Major. It's like her whole body exhales with the first puff and swallow. 'It's their day. Their Holy day.'

I can't let it pass, I've always hated that dopey religious solemnity. 'Bunch of freaks and throwbacks' I say, but quietly. People are unpredictable in Kerry, in pubs especially.

'Ah go away, you'll go to hell for that, may God forgive you.' But her eyes are sparkling. For a devout woman, she always gets a kick out of my irreverence.

It's full dark when we come back out. We walk past the phone box, too late to ring Daddy. We walk up the wrong end of the road, away from the Centra with the ice-cream machine, with the big rotating 99 with a flake on top of it, the chipper and the caravan sites. It's pitch black outside, the swirling light of the street lamps and the hardware shops at this end of the village are unfamiliar. The wind has a tang of the sea in it, the mountains are dark humps in the distance. Everything feels old and lonely, like the land around us doesn't need us or want us. We walk closer together instinctively, even though we never touch each other usually. I can feel the energy radiating out of her small, narrow body and I feel nervous. What if she won't go back on Sunday, like we're supposed to? What if we miss the train in Killarney? Daddy will have to come all the way down here to get us, what will he do with the rest of them? There'll be murder. I wish I'd made her get me another hamburger.

It's like she's reading my thoughts. 'We'll get you another burger when they open tomorrow.' There's a light smell of Carling beer floating alongside us, it's coming off her, she's taking in great big gulps of air in the darkness. 'The sea air. Make sure you breathe it in. Han used to say 'tis very good for you.' She sounds satisfied. I'm not used to it. The sea is up the other end of the village, but I imagine the black waves beating on the shore in the darkness. I can feel the faint thump of them coming up through the soles of my feet as we're walking.

The Pattern is small, as it was always going to be. A group of red-faced parishioners follow the priest down through the village, past The White Sands on one side, the chipper and the Centra on the other, up to the steps that lead down to the

36

water, the beginning of a long strand that curves in a perfect horseshoe out along the bay, and is lit golden on the one or two days when the sun shines in the summer. We pick our way along the clifftop, careful as the white goats that look down on us from rocky outcroppings, chewing as we shuffle along beneath them. Mammy smells of Silvermints with her head bowed, as we bring up the rear in a tide of farmers. At the well, the grass is still dewy, soaking my jeans past my ankles. White lilies bloom on either side of the rushy pool that's thick with bright green algae and dotted with elegant pond skaters describing figures of eight in the still water, the only creatures moving. People are quietly, rhymically mouthing a Rosary. I pick up the edges of the Hail Mary, saying only the bits that don't freak me out. Once you know about periods, 'Blessed is the fruit of thy womb' is always a bit disgusting. The virgin sits beside the green pool on her bed of woven palms, sad and serene in her white robes, her crown of stars, a blue tear on each cheek. You'd have thought being the mother of God would have its upsides, but she is always crying – on her own or draped across His broken body.

'Pray for us sinners, now and at the hour of our death. Amen.' Carol's long fingernails are painted pink with a faint sparkle. Rimmel varnish, from the chemist, in the rustly white paper bag with the twisty snake on it. She always does them perfectly. She is full of the excitement of being with the villagers. 'Sure I always loved Kerry people – my Mam's people are Kerry,' she'll insist, as though I've claimed she didn't. I watch the crowd for some speck of sophistication, but everyone looks like farmers, ruddy and deferential, heads bowed, caps twisted around in big slabby fists. A few have full heads of springy grey curls that seem to pop up like horns on either side of their faces, like centaurs.

Afterwards, we go back to the same corner of Lehane's, while she soaks up what she insists on calling the atmosphere, and I drink a cold Coke and wait for the chipper to open. I get two burgers, and she lets me take them back to the B&B by myself. It's nice to turn at the door and see her talk to strangers, loose and easy, smiling even. 'We're only down for the Pattern, ourselves, but my mother's originally from Glenbeigh' she's saying, the third time that day I've heard it.

A revelation, her volunteering information so easily. Back up in Cork, she sits in the lounges, golden pint in front of her, mouth locked up in sour judgement. She'll talk to the boy or the girl behind the bar, but her antennae are exquisitely delicate – as soon as she detects a hint of a reservation in any of them, at the sight of a woman drinking in the middle of the day, accompanied by one or more children in school uniforms, pleasantries will be suspended abruptly. But this is not Cork, this is Kerry. My last glimpse is of her obligingly moving along in her seat for an old man who'd been standing in front of us during the Rosary. She's listening intently to whatever he is saying, her face full of interest and no defences.

I am happy then, because she is happy, even though we've already spent a few nights this summer tearing at each other around my bedroom. I remember the shock of enjoyment the first time I dug my fingers through her hair, grabbed a thick handful close to her scalp and pulled until she screamed high like a wounded rabbit. She grabbed mine in retaliation, and we stood braced against each other for a couple of agonising seconds, locked together, mirror images of each other. I never kicked her, I remember that – I only tore, and scratched, bit her once or twice even. I only wanted to use sharp things on her, wound her, pierce her. We're well matched, she's tiny.

But I am happy for her that night in Lehane's, happy to leave her there in the smoky throng of the pub. I wait beneath the fluorescent lights for my burgers, think about taking them up and eating them in front of the tumbling ocean. But I am a bit scared of the sea at night, the things that could come out of it, the ways it has of catching you in the darkness, so I stuff the grey paper packet under my cardigan, and it keeps me warm the whole way back to the edge of the village. I slip in the door of the house with the green windows, silently so the woman won't hear me. I get into my single bed and eat the burgers methodically, one after the other, watching the cold rain splatter against the windows, wondering what my sister and brothers are doing. I think about the farmers filling the streets that morning, thumping their chests reverently, walking behind Jesus's mother.

Six

From the bottom of the hill you can't see where the school is
meant to be. I'm out at the edge of town, towards the train
station, pubs and nightclubs on either side of me – proper city
pubs with double rows of kegs out front and trad sessions for
Americans on a Monday. It's just before 9am and I am full of
excitement and the confidence of having prepared properly.
Up at quarter past seven, before the new alarm clock went off,
even. White Musk shower gel, hair back in a high ponytail.
Uniform on, piece by piece carefully, lifting it off the hanger
on the door of the wardrobe where she hung it. We did the
change for the bus last night, counting out her pile of tarnished
gold 20-pences. Daddy tried to give me a fiver when he
came in, leaning on the bedroom door, hiccuping delicately 'For
tomorrow, just take it, sure' waving it over. 'They won't break
a note, you have to have the coins,' I said, taking the money.
He shambled off to his bed, Mammy materialising behind him.

'He hasn't a clue, don't mind him. Sure when does he get buses?' 'And he never went to secondary school' – I know she wanted to say it, but she didn't.

Her excitement filled the kitchen this morning. I felt it going down, a sparkling, uncharacteristic current of happiness coming up the stairs to meet me. She walked into the kitchen through the arch from the front room, where she'd been staring at the bus stop over the road from us. 'Your toast is there.' Pointing unnecessarily at the little plate of it, cut into careful triangles, the glass of orange juice, out of the can for me, especially. She moves so quietly, you can't even hear her.

This is the time of day when I almost like her. Smoking in her jumpers and tracksuit pants – 'my work clothes' she calls them, cheap thin clothes in soft muddy colours. Watching her washing through the kitchen window, still deep down in herself, letting the new day gather its momentum. They said I wouldn't need a lunch, but it's there for me. 'Fresh bread, and the Denny's ham, the good one, in the packet. I only got it yesterday.' I sigh exaggeratedly, put the tinfoil packet into my bag. I like a ham sandwich. 'Go on so, you don't want to miss it.' She waves her fag at the gold clock on the wall. There's twenty minutes before the bus I'm getting, according to the timetable folded in the top pocket of my new blazer. But I don't want to miss it either. I lever my bag onto my back, reach over and kiss her cheek, warm with the blood flowing into it. I pick up the last piece of toast, sagging in the middle with a puddle of butter, open the front door, and close it softly behind me.

St Angela's. 'Nose up, knickers down' is the unofficial school motto. No fees per se, but an annual parents' donation. Daddy leaves it for me in cash in an envelope on the kitchen table. At the start of August, Mammy and I pore over the orientation information. We go together, to a small shop down a side street

41

in the middle of town, choose a second-hand blazer from a rack that hangs down from the ceiling. Green and tweedy, it doesn't suit me. It doesn't suit anyone, that's not the point. The point of the blazer is to signal that this is a school that takes itself seriously. A school with a pedigree, a school that has been educating the daughters of this city for over one hundred years – girls from houses in Monkstown, Glanmire, Rochestown, Douglas, houses with names, not numbers, in quiet leafy suburbs overlooking the water. Houses that had been inherited, or designed by architects, houses full of books with no toilets and sinks and pipes lying around in the back garden. We bought the blazer and the skirt too big on purpose. The woman nodded. 'You have to get the wear out of it.' Two shirts, brand new in rustling plastic, light green with darker green stripes. Later, I'd learn to roll the skirt up at the waist – once, twice, three times – until a generous length of thigh was showing. Push the green socks down my calves like the Fifth and Sixth years. On that first day, though, I went up that hill modest as a nun, my socks meeting my lumpy skirt at the kneecap.

I don't know when Mammy decided on it, how she heard about the place even. She went to secondary school up the road from her house, with the nuns in North Presentation. I wanted to go to St Vincent's, where all my friends were going, not a stuck-up school in the city with an outlandish green uniform. I only knew one other girl going there. It was full, in any case, they told her. She got me on a waiting list. And then she wore them down, an exhaustive, patient process involving weekly phone calls, and at least one trek up the hill to see the principal. Like summiting Everest, the way she tells it. But just before my confirmation, a call on the creamy white phone hanging off the wall in the kitchen. 'Mrs McCarthy, a place has become available. We've decided to offer it to your daughter.' She acts it out for me repeatedly, making her voice high pitched and posh to imitate Miss O'Shea. 'Very plain, God love her, but a nice woman. Very nice, in fairness.'

'Well, that's it now,' she says some evenings, taking a deep, satisfied sigh, 'you're going to St Angela's. Your education – all of ye're education – that's up to me, girl. No, I'm dead serious.' Over and over again, evening after evening, whenever she could get me in front of her. Shaking her head at any challenge, real or imagined. 'Your father knows it. Sure, he hasn't a clue, he doesn't.' I get out then, usually, before she starts going on about how his pants were held up with twine when she met him.

Climbing the hill, there's a burn low down in my legs, near my ankles, a stretch like I've never felt before. It's exhilarating. I turn around, and I'm directly over the widest bridge in the city. Cars and buses crawl up and down Patrick Street in opposite directions, the grey quay where I got off my bus is washed in morning sunlight, the domes of the shopping centre towering over it. It's how the city would look in a snow globe, if you squashed it. The school is a collection of houses behind a high gate near the top of the hill. Walking through in my uniform, I feel the thrill of chosenness.

Long blonde hair, these girls have, hair that shines like money. They carry canvas bags, long and awkward, with blue or red stripes and the name MCWILLIAM printed on them. Sailing bags, I don't realise until I see them in a sports shop a few years later. All the money in Cork has always been spent on the water. They know each other already, from the small, fee-paying primary school behind the secondary school buildings, or from other schools in suburbs of the Southside, places my Dad would come out in hives if he had to spend any time in. Places I know the names of, but in no way connect with the city I live in. I talk to a girl called Áine – there are lots of Áines and Aoifes and Niamhs, even a Dearbhall. This Áine has red hair and silver glasses and freckles, and is just back from Brittany. Her mother teaches French, she says, and her Dad is a lecturer at the university. 'Mum' and 'Dad', she calls them, without a possessive. All of them do it, I explain to Mammy later at home when I'm doing an impersonation of Áine, making my voice high and nasal, stretching out my vowels: 'We went to Fraaance for the summer.'

'And we went to Ballyheigue, says you.' Mammy puts on the same posh accent. 'And did she ask what your father does? He's a plumber, and he makes fine money, tell her.' She ashes her fag defiantly. 'They'd call him quick enough when their toilets are broken.' Later, when the hilarity has died down and her mood curdles, she shouts up the stairs to me: 'You're as good as any of them, girl, don't ever forget it.'

This is the year I start wearing Daddy's clothes. He is double, if not triple my weight, and a good eight or nine inches taller than me, besides being a father of four and a working plumber. I want to blame grunge but in the early '90s in Ireland, nobody in my orbit was properly grungy. We hadn't yet heard of Nirvana, or anything harder than Red Hot Chilli Peppers. It's the volume of the clothes that I like, their potential as drapery. I wear a grey tweed waistcoat to the beach once, that's how self-conscious I am. I tie a scarf around my neck, because women in books who do this are described as elegant, but it only seems to make my face look fatter. I have small breasts finally, after years of staring down my crop top in fruitless supplication, but other parts of my body are still a problem. I am soft and solid around the middle – some boys start calling me the Barrel. I cut out two pictures from a magazine, one of Yasmin Le Bon topless in a pair of white bikini bottoms, and one of agony aunt Claire

Rayner holding up a glass of sherry, and I write WHAT YOU WANT and WHAT YOU DON'T WANT under them. I diet by only having apples instead of popcorn when we're watching videos. I like the powerful feeling I get from not eating, but give in quickly for toast, or chips and biscuits.

I wear Daddy's rugby shirt under his sports coat, which is what Cork people call a kind of suit jacket. It is a black-and-white herringbone tweed and I like the shape and the protective weight of it across my shoulders. I pin badges from The Body Shop along both collars. I go to The Body Shop every Saturday, buying soaps in the shapes of whales and giraffes and signing petitions against animal testing. One of my friends does a Jeremy Bentham quote for me in calligraphy: 'The question is not, Can they reason? nor Can they think? But, Can they suffer?' I put it over the side of my bed. Some of the commas are in the wrong place, but I love it.

I wear the rugby shirt with jeans and loafers to the Beat on The Street, a mobile disco put on by a radio station on the Lee Fields every summer. A DJ on a platform blasts out singles for a crowd of teenagers from dusk until proper dark. We jump around on the squelchy grass of the low-lying river plain, the music pounding through the soles of our shoes, while over on the far bank of the river, the long stone corridors of the madhouse – St Anne's – loom over us. The finale is always Livin' On A Prayer. If you were getting off with someone, that's when it would happen, fireworks blooming red and purple and orange in the night sky above you. I never get a shift, but it's enough just to be out late, roaming home up through Sunday's Well and along Blarney Street with the rest of them. It's the summer of Atlantic 252, the pirate longwave radio station – I hear the first bars of Crucify on 252. Its delicate piano and strange, religious imagery stop me dead in front of my radio cassette player. I wait and wait, until I finally catch it from the start and tape it. I listen to that song until I can dream the lyrics in their entirety. And then I see Tori Amos on MTV at my friend Jennifer's house, and she looks crazy, spreadeagled in front of her piano, flinging her long red hair around, not caring. I don't want to like her after that, she scares me. But I keep on playing the song over and over, patiently untangling the spools of tape when they get snarled in the metal teeth of the tape deck, circling them back up into the cassette with a pencil.

We kiss the boys we hang around with two estates over in rituals that are simple and ancient. I play Dares along with everyone else, in a field beside the steps where we meet every evening. Colin O'Keefe is my first dare. He puts his mouth on mine and leaves it there. My lips and cheeks smell like John Player Blue afterwards. Mark Foley is next, my secret crush – he looks like Tom Cruise in *Risky Business*. He moves his mouth in a small soft circle and I follow to the best of my ability. The ones who come after are jabbing tongues, and varying degrees of dryness and wetness. I never kiss any of them again, after that one game. Michelle, who is tall with long black hair and a beautiful smile that you want to make happen as often as possible, is the first to have a proper boyfriend. Ritchie has a shaved head, with a few blond spikes at the front, walks his dad's dog on a piece of leather and listens to Bob Marley. A grown man, essentially.

Mammy tolerates me spending my evenings over at the steps that summer. 'You'll be back in St Angela's in September, you'll have your own friends there,' she'll say, more to herself than anyone, when she sees me with my hand on the front door in the evenings. I leave her there on the sofa, or at the kitchen table, with her cans of Tuborg tucked in beside her discreetly. 'And ye'll meet those boys from Christians I suppose, down in the Vic pool hall. Woo-hoo!' she whoops in a parody of playground teasing.

Mammy is happy when a school friend invites me on my first sleepover – she's as desperate as I am to see what everyone's houses look like. The house has a number, not a name, but it's big all the same. On this estate, every house sits alone at the top of a smoothly curving drive, like a fat white cake. Daddy drops me, happy not to have to go in and meet anyone. The Dad is some kind of businessman, not a plumber. The front door opens, and Catriona's smiling at me from a wide hallway. Stairs curl up behind her, so much space on either side. We walk through the kitchen, pass through into a formal living room. It's dark, I can only make out the vague shapes of white sofas, a marble fireplace bouncing car lights off it. The same black night pushes against the windows that I walked out into earlier, but up here, out of the city, the air is as clean and fresh as all of these furniture and fittings. The family – Mam and Dad, two younger brothers – are all sitting in a smaller lounge behind the main one. It's a much more approachable space, bright and slightly shabbier, with a coal bucket on the hearth, the TV on and the fire going. But then we go upstairs, and Catriona's bedroom has its own landing. She has an en suite too. She's never coming to my house. But I already knew this. A few of the girls from school have invited me to their homes, for dinners, and birthdays. Mammy doesn't even pretend I should return the invitations.

Catriona is in my home-class, she has shiny black hair and shiny green eyes and, even though she talks a lot, there is something pleasing and vital about her that outweighs the annoyingness of her confidence. I am drawn to her because she is quick, and pretty. At the age of 13, I know full well that I am shallow. I tell myself, it's because I like reading so much, I'm drawn to characters. I've already been bowling with Catriona, for her birthday. I'm pleased she keeps asking me places, even though I never reciprocate. In a year or so, when I read her diary,

I will see how much she truly likes me. She is glad we are friends, my opinion of her matters. I read this with a happy sense of gratification that feels like safety. I am always snooping in these girls' bedrooms, reading things I shouldn't be. I feel like I am justified in spying to have this information. I can't even help it – it's instinctive. It feels important to know what the girls at school think of me, if I am doing things correctly.

This was a while before teenagers had personal mobile phones. I am grateful for that now. If they'd had them, I would have read them.

Seven

I get the book out of the school library. It's just another high-ceilinged room in the draughty old house where the First Years are, but it's always quiet, with golden light coming through the bay windows and the air full of the smell of old paper. You can take what you want once you write it in the ledger. *Dracula*. On the cover there's a man with black hair in a comically deep widow's peak, red eyes and a mouthful of teeth like daggers. Gravestones in the shape of crosses tilting behind him. A circle of fog, or dry ice swirling around his ankles. Penguin Classic, children's edition. Unabridged though.

Jonathan Harker's Journal (Kept in Shorthand)

3 May. Bistritz. Left Munich at 8.35p.m. on 1st May, arriving at Vienna early next morning [. . .] Buda-pesth seems a wonderful place, from the glimpse which I got of it from the train. [. . .] The impression I had was that we were leaving the West and entering the East.

Poor posho Jonathan Harker. Three chapters in, already locked up in a castle with a monster.

Up the tight loops of the curling white staircase, book hugged close to me. German class, looking out over the city, the grey stone spread of it, inching towards the horizon. Nominativ, dativ, akkusativ. Subject, object, verb with calm, plain Mrs Prendergast. Someone said her son got the full 600 points in the Leaving. The glass in the windows is warped, old as the worm-eaten desks we sit at. Rain distorts the view through the panes even further. 'Wie komme ich am besten zum Bahnhof bitte?'

Down to the prefabs for English after. Weak spring sun trying to come out, dry out the rain-slicked basketball court, bitumen sparkling. I'm at the back, book flat on the desk.

Chapter II – This is Transylvania, and Transylvania is not England. Our ways are not your ways, and there shall be to you many strange things.

'Good morning girls.' Mrs Brennan, in full sail, striding to the top of the room, shaking back her shaggy hair. Something leonine in her, not just her mane, the wide gape of her jaws when she's laughing, which she does often. Hands together, eyes closed. 'All right girls: In the name of the Father, and of the Son.' Scrape of our chairs, shambles of 25 voices trying to find a rhythm. At least she never makes a meal of it, Mrs Hartnett would make you do a novena if she could. Eyes still closed, she's pulling down the cuffs on the white shirt she wears every day, mannish but it suits her – she must have a wardrobe full of them.

'But deliver us from evil. Amen. Would you open that window Jackie, 'tis very close.'

'Ah Miss, we're frozen.' Orla O'Riordan, shivering under two borrowed scarves and a jacket.

'Nonsense,' laughing her deep laugh. 'Take those scarves off you, activate your circulatory system Orla.'

Our essays are passed back down, neat black scrawl on the ends and in the margins. Mrs Brennan's comments are memorable. 'Sadly adequate' was always the one I dreaded. But I was on a roll that year. 'Noelle, I've run out of superlatives,' she wrote, for a tragic attempt at a ghost story, not long after *Dracula*.

After English, PE with Lynchie. She has a culchie accent – from Limerick, or Tipperary – and small eyes of an arctic blue that would go through you. She wears a tracksuit most days, with frosted pink lipstick and a heavy gold medal from some Gaelic football game she won years ago. I fear her. We jump over sawhorses and do forward rolls on dusty parquet. It's a free class after PE. I come back once the gym is empty, settle down on a pile of blue plastic mats that smell of feet and Impulse body spray. Harker makes it to London, his spirit broken. Dracula reaches England too, and menaces beautiful, vivacious Lucy. She is found wandering the laneways of Whitby, distressed and half dressed, by her friend Mina Murray. Mina is clever, kind and resourceful and she wants to be a journalist. Maybe that's where I first heard of it. The rain leaves off, the sun climbs higher, streaming in through the streaky sash windows lighting up the back wall mural, a full-scale representation of St Veronica wiping the face of Jesus. When you jump over the sawhorses it's Jesus's blessed face on her washcloth you're facing. Outside the gym, the bell clangs, shaken on a long piece of washing line by one of the Third Years chosen for the job specially. *I want you to believe*, Van Helsing says to the others.

I walk with a book pressed up to my face over the next day or so, fearing every minute I am going to go over a step, or into one of the fussy beds of pansies outside the classrooms. Knowing how stupid it must look, how ostentatiously nerdy. But nobody really cares about that kind of thing in St Angela's. Everyone is always having Amnesty International meetings at lunch break, organising fasts for Africa. I keep the book to my face as I walk from room to room. Lucy dies, and is staked by her prospective husband. The vampire is pursued through London. And then, without preamble or warning, Dracula uses a long fingernail to slice a vein in his chest open. He pushes Mina's face down into it. I run up the back stairs to the old art room, my heart thumping. I sit in one of the empty desks, blowing little flecks of dried-up paint off it, next to a jam jar full of brushes. Someone's maths class is droning on the other side of the wall to me. My head is buzzing. I don't know how long I sit there, bathed in weak turpentine fumes, falling deeper and deeper into the desperate pursuit of the vampire. Following his dirt-filled coffins as they bob across the Black Sea, hypnotised Mina continuing to provide a link to him. And she has been made unclean by the contact. The communion wafer burns her forehead. My stomach twists with pity.

At some stage school is over. I go home on the bus, still reading. This is risky on the Number 2, someone might rip the book off you. But on this day, I dare them. 'We go out in God's name,' Van Helsing reminds the others before the final showdown. The tears in my eyes surprise me. Nearly home already. Estates flash by, the view out the window starts looking greener.

Am I still reading *Dracula* when we do our first dissection? Sitting in the lab, next to the sinks, and the copper bunsen burners, picking up the scalpel, the metal cold through the thin membrane of latex gloves we'd pulled from a long, flat cardboard packet. Slicing through the big cow heart in front of me, the fat that marbled the outside of it thick and pearly as candle wax. Left ventricle, right ventricle. Vena Cava. Pulmonary veins. Aorta.

'And remember about the different colours? Bright red blood in arteries, the blood in veins is deoxygenated so it's darker red, more like purple.'

Miss Murphy, our science teacher, has wide brown eyes, neat spiral curls, pretty like Lucy Westenra. She has a soft Kerry accent and a fluting voice, something happening to her breath when it reached her front teeth, just the faintest whistle on the enamel. She has her own big heart in front of her, demonstrating the strokes for us. I take my scalpel in my fingers, holding it like a pencil, feel the thrill of it. I think of long fine teeth, the vampire's mouth opening. I push down just a little bit harder on the scalpel and the heart opens up like a flower. The flesh is puckered, pale pink, drained of blood days earlier.

Strangely enough, I did not want to hinder him, says Mina, when the vampire drinks from her.

The big heart smells like the meat Mammy gets from the butcher's on Shandon Street, sweet and gamey. There is a stronger whiff from this one though, a fleshy, heavy sourness, you wouldn't want to roast it. We follow Miss Murphy, sticking our gloved fingers into the rubbery aorta, making notes in the red and black experiment notebooks she's been making us keep for months now, labelling the chambers according to the diagrams in *Science Alive!* The vampire, being both dead, and alive, defies the laws of biology, chemistry and physics. He is disruptive, he won't stay dead. He is dangerous. He is hungry.

Some time later. A Wednesday maybe. After lunch break. Physical geography. Lynchie again, with her medal and her pink lipstick, rat-a-tat-ing at the top of the class. Limestone karst formations, glaciers. The Burren. In the cold yellow shed out the back of the prefabs I sit down on the clammy toilet seat and there's blood on my knickers. Not bright and flowing, just a rusty smear of it. Brown, and drying darker as the air hits it. I stare down, stupefied, as surprised as if I'd found a pile of leaves or feathers in my underwear. I feel the cramps start as I am staring at it. Dull and insistent, low down in my belly. I pull the metal chain high up over my head and the cistern shudders. Water flows into the bowl, obliterating all traces. I go back to class, a wad of scratchy grey toilet paper rustling against me.

At home, I tell Mammy quickly, get it over with. I can see her moving her mouth, trying to decide what to say, wanting to say everything, barely containing it. She goes into her bedroom, comes back with a full packet of sanitary towels, Stayfree in blue writing on the front and a wispy image of a girl in a big straw hat with ribbons on it. Big silky bricks of things, with an adhesive strip down the middle – you pull off the thin paper backing and it flips back and sticks to your fingers. I hate it. She goes downstairs and comes back with a white plastic supermarket bag.

'Put this under your bed. When you change yourself, put the used ones in there and I'll come and empty it – privately.'

I want to say, can't I just stick the bag behind the bath like you do, but she's whispering and pursing her lips up delicately when she says 'privately', like she does every time she lectures me about periods, or getting breasts, or salt baths for when you're sore 'underneath' and I just can't cope with it so I take the plastic bag, and the packet of pads, and I change them scrupulously every four hours, even though I have to gasp and hold my breath at the mess and the state and the smell of it. I hate the way the bag rustles every time I put a dirty pad in it. 'You've had a grand heavy period, Noelle,' Mammy tries to come in and say, solemnly, half-cut one night. I slam the door on her.

'I was only leaving you fresh stuff I got in Dunnes for you! For all the thanks I get.' Muttered. Once she's gone, I open the door and drag the pads in furtively, like an animal, slamming the door again behind me. I hate her knowing what my body is doing.

Twilight. I'm in bed already, under the floral bedspread I picked out myself from Roches Stores. When I went to St Angela's, we did up the guest room for me. Sage-green walls with a floral trim at waist level, a desk under my bookshelves, black-and-white Athena posters. To the left of where I lie, in my narrow single bed, the window is open. This is deliberate. I want Dracula to visit. I watch the thin curtain bell in and out with the evening breeze, my lashes half lowered. There's a faint light in the sky, it's the start of summer, it won't be dark till 10 o'clock these nights. I close my eyes, thinking of Mina, thinking of Lucy. *Strangely enough, I did not want to hinder him.*

I need to be asleep, or at least, walking that wavy line between full sleep and half waking. I don't know exactly what he would do when he comes in the window. That's lies, I know he would bite me. The thin flesh of my neck just above my collarbone pricks up with wanting. It is pleasurable. The vampire, when he comes, can overpower me, do what he wants to me, and I will let him. He is welcome. I am ready. Our house is uncharacteristically quiet. On the nights when she doesn't go to town in the afternoon, Mammy is often tired and goes to bed early. My door is safely closed. The wind sucks the curtain through the open window, pushes it back through again, billowing. Outside, I can hear the thump of cars on the road, the heavier drag of the bus going up towards Apple Computers. A dog barks, frantically, for a few seconds and stops just as suddenly. The light bleeds out of the sky. Everything in my room becomes an outline. In the morning, I will get up, push play on the REM tape in my white boom box, put on my green uniform while Michael Stipe sings Don't Go Back to Rockville. I will get the Number 2 at ten past eight, a few others in school uniforms and the wall-eyed shift workers from the computer factory. But for now, I lie very still in my bed, trembling and waiting. I turn my face away from the window, look over at my desk. A fussy little jar I got for my birthday or for Christmas, stands on a cream doily. The lid is a glass dolphin breaching, its tail curving out of the water. Inside, it is full of little balls, like marbles, blue, green, pink. As the room gets darker, it becomes impossible to distinguish the pale milky colours. Orange headlights slice across the curtains. I keep waiting, holding my body ready in the pale silk pyjamas with waterlilies I got for Christmas, my hair fanned as attractively as possible across the pillow. I try to catch myself at the moment of falling asleep but I miss it.

He never comes. Not that night, not the night after. Not any of the nights I wait, even though I keep my window open so often, all the decorative squirrels and hedgehogs I collected fall off the windowsill. I nearly dislocate my fingers, reaching down the back of the rads to get them. I read the book again. I read other ghost stories, just to make sure there isn't some trick I missed, some other summoning ritual. You have to invite them. I whisper it some nights, into my pillow. And then swallow the words, because they sound silly. Come in, come in. Come and get me. I don't see his face in my dreams, unlike Lucy. But I know what he looks like. High, aquiline nose, thick brows, dark eyes. An aristocrat. Not like the boys over on Hillcrest Steps. None of them like me, knew what to make of me. The day Trevor Hackett steals my shoe and pisses into it, my body goes cold all over. If this was a story, I'd make him pay, is all I could think of, when they kick it back down the road to me. My first pair of platforms, a thin streak of piss running out of them. Someone wipes them out with grass, one of the girls taking pity on me. I must have worn them walking back over home. Maybe I took off the other one, and walked it barefoot.

'You think you're better than all of us, anyway,' Alan says to me one night over at the steps. Alan is handsome, with blonde hair and green eyes, some of the girls had already played dares with him, I want him to kiss me. But he's leaning over the handlebars of his bike, squinting up at me like I'm another species.

I lie in bed. I want a vampire to come in my window and lean over me. His hair is black, his expression a mix of contempt and desire. I will open the neck of my peach pyjamas. I will lie back ready. I want a vampire to sense me, lying here behind the open window of this semi-detached pebble-dash four-bedroom. I want him to have me, turn me, rescue me.

'If I catch you at your hair again, I'll hop the head off you.'

He flings whatever is in his hand at me, something long and plastic. It misses, sailing in an arc well wide of the mark, smashing into the side of the fish tank. A warning shot more than anything. I glare over at him, the blood in my chest pumping in readiness. He's standing, tongue tucked and wide legged in the kitchen, under the arch she somehow convinced him to knock into the wall so no matter what room you're in you have to listen to her. One of his hands is opening and closing spasmodically, missing whatever was in it. The spatula for the frying pan, I can smell rashers cooking. I stand very still. He knows. How does he know? He can't have noticed. Black Cherry my arse, apart from a slight purple tinge in direct sunlight, you can barely see any difference. He stares me down, nostrils flaring, fingers twitching. I do a quick scan of what else might be nearby for flinging. 'I mean it, don't touch it again, do you hear me?' Jabbing at me with one of his big banana fingers.

Mammy's voice in my ear, standing in front of me upstairs in the bathroom while I still had the plastic gloves on. 'Don't let him catch you, you know what he's like over hair. I'm telling you now girl, there'll be murder.' Shaking her head at me, my hair in a pile on top of my head clotted with what looks like stage blood. She walks down the stairs, washing her hands of me, pulling the sides of her cardigan together like a shawlie. I gave it forty minutes, like the packet said. Jennifer laughed at me when I complained to her. 'Don't be so stupid, you've to leave it on for an hour. It's not working 'til your scalp starts burning.'

I open my mouth better to fill my lungs with air, working myself up to it. He's still in front of me, in his shirt and good jeans for a Saturday morning, ones that don't have the back pockets blown out from constantly bending over. His eyes are wild. A few years ago he'd probably have taken a run at me, slapped my legs or my arse or whatever he could get hold of – but now I am older and bigger and invested with my own authority. The curls are damp either side of his forehead. 'LEAVE ME ALONE,' I bellow, with all the breath in my body. The china cups in their cabinet shake a little in admiration. 'Leave me alone, you're always at me!' And then I burst into noisy tears, throw myself out of the front room, gallop up the stairs on all fours like I have done all of my life whenever I am challenged.

I can see what's happened as soon as I get in there. The cupboard above my built-in dresser is open. I swing myself up on top of the dresser, and pull myself up. The packet of hair dye, a sketch of a red-lipped woman with a burgundy-coloured bob on the front, has been pulled out from the back of the cupboard where I shoved it, as well as the instructions, covered with purple fingerprints. Worse, much worse, is the blue-and-pink-striped box of Tampax next to it. I stare down at the folded-up leaflet, open at the little line drawings of how a tampon is inserted. Up and back, through the vagina, the lower intestine a curly tube above the cervix. Daddy saw all this. My cheeks burn as hot blood floods them.

I haven't even used any, only bought a box to look at them. Jennifer and her sister use non-applicator ones, I've seen them in her bathroom. That felt too advanced, I was comforted by the idea of the applicator. I've had the box there for a month and taken one out of its wrapping, seen how the cardboard tubes slotted into each other cleverly. Mammy said 'Those things are only for women who are married already.' She found some in Auntie Cay's drawer once and always held it against her.

'Don't be so stupid,' I said, the one time I engaged her on the subject. 'They're a normal form of sanitary protection.'

'You don't know what you're talking about, they're English magazines you're reading!' she shouted back up the stairs at me.

And now, there they are, rolling around in broad daylight at the bottom of my cupboard, long white bullets in their silky paper packaging, TAMPAX written up the side in yellow. How could he have found them? He'd never go looking. He didn't, I knew it. She opened that fucking cupboard.

'How dare you!' she rose up, an O-faced martyr, when I stamped into her bedroom, where she was sitting there smoking, looking out the window. 'On my life to God, I didn't open anything, Sure how would I know what you have in that cupboard? Why would I go near your stuff?' She was shouting now, waving the Major. 'Go away girl, you're wronging me.'

'You did! You knew where it was and you showed him!' Stamping my feet, full of the electric charge of hating her.

'I told you, I told you! He gets very bad about hair! All his life with ye.'

It's true, he didn't speak to anyone for two days when I was 12 and got a haircut. In fairness, the woman didn't know anything about curly hair and tried to put layers in it. My head looked like a Christmas tree a child would draw, a series of triangles piled on top of each other. This was the woman who did my mother's hair, whose preparation for the application of colour consisted of daubing a thick ring of cigarette ash along Mammy's forehead. My mother does what she likes with her hair, cuts it short and tight, gets highlights painted on through a cap that sits on her crown like a jellyfish, has perms that make her look electrocuted, as is statutory requirement in the '80s, but my father polices our hair jealously. My sister could sit on her hair for most of her life. To this day he gets a bit downcast if she turns up with anything above her shoulders.

'It's something to do with his mother,' Mammy whispers, flicking her eyes down through the floor to where he is cooking the rashers below us. 'A thing he has. I told you not to do it. But no, you're always the same. You just won't do as you're told, ever. Well, I'm staying out of it now. There's nothing I can do about it.'

She sucks on the fag ruefully, turns back to the window. I stamp back into my room, climb back up on the dresser and push everything as far to the back of the top cupboard as I can get it. Stray tampons roll back towards me, there's a slight lean in the joinery. I slam the door shut, turn on music. At 5 o'clock she leaves my dinner on the landing and I ignore it. Around seven there's a different knock, slower and heavier. I wait until I hear his heavy step going back down the stairs before I open. Next to the plate of chops and potatoes, neon carrots and congealed gravy on the Ninja Turtles TV tray, is a brown bag from Burger King. There's a purple 20-pound note half pushed halfway under the door as well. I pull the note out, pick up the bag, and close the door behind me. A Chicken Royale with no mayo. Exactly how I like it.

Eight

You go into a room, and you open the piece of paper you've been given. On it, there's a sentence with a question mark at the end of it. If Ireland was right to join the EEC, if a little learning is a dangerous thing, or whether heaven on earth is a possibility. You sit down, and you write for 15, 20, 30 minutes, something like that, on the proposition. Then you go into a room full of people and give a speech to them. This is extemporaneous public speaking. Mrs Brennan got me into it. She brings a group of us to a hotel in the middle of the city. The Fifth and Sixth Years don't talk to us, they go with a different group and we don't see them. The other girls my age are like me: nervous, but willing.

After I write my speech, on a topic I don't remember, I wait for a few minutes until the door opens and someone calls me. I follow them out into a bigger room, and walk up onto a low stage at the far end of it. I put my notes down on a lectern, and look up finally, conscious of nothing, but the sudden, unfamiliar sense of time slowing. I am able to notice everything. The still, stale air of the conference room, with its old fashioned moulded ceiling and fussy red-and-gold wallpaper. The soft grey light and the bobbing shadows of pigeons through the pale blinds pulled down over floor-length windows. The beeping of traffic lights, and the hiss of tyres on a wet road on the street below us.

In front of me is an audience, older men mostly. White hair, dark suits, soft pink cheeks, big hands and noses. Cork City Speakers Club. Farmers, teachers, accountants. I open my mouth and start talking to them. My speech is written down in front of me; I don't use it. As I talk, new ideas come into my head and I am able to find the right words to express them. I speak in paragraphs, pause at the right moments – I don't know how I am able to do this. Along the back of the room is a long narrow table covered in a white cloth that glows in the gloomy light like an altar. There's a big silver urn on it, and an expansive spread of white bone china cups and saucers. The room is full of the smell of coffee, bitter and warm and energising. I've never tasted coffee, but I like how it smells like something is about to happen. I stand in front of the men, and I talk and I talk, about something I've since forgotten – politics, or human rights, or motorways. At two-and-a-half minutes a bell rings. I've been told this will happen. For the remaining thirty seconds, I weave threads together furiously, working my way towards a conclusion that feels there for the taking. The bell rings a second time, louder and more urgently, as I am finishing my last sentence. The men lean forward, pull the fabric of their trousers over the tops of their thighs where it has settled. There's a sense of something being let free in the room, a little bird flying over us, as they clap their clean white hands together. I pick up my papers, and step down off the stage. My cheeks are red and hot when I put my hands up to them. I know without having to be told that I have done exactly what has been asked of me. I know this is a facility, a physical thing more than anything, like being a good singer or dancer. I did not know I had it. At the end of the afternoon, the judge says the final will be in some school on the Southside in a month's time. I will be in it.

Mrs Brennan stands at the back, beside the white table, with a cup of milky coffee and a saucerful of wet red grapes and plain biscuits. 'Very good, very good, well done,' she says, not only to me, but to everyone. Later she says 'We'll practise, I'll give you topics' to me and another girl who's got through to the final. When I win the final, she smiles her wide-jawed smile, a happy lion. She shakes the hands of the teachers of the other finalists. I get a small trophy and a silver medallion on a fat blue silky rope on a satin cushion that says JUNIOR CHAMPION. There will be a dinner, with speeches from me and the senior winner, in another, fancy old stuffy hotel in the city. I buy a dress that buttons up the middle, quite low cut but still seemly, in a black cotton fabric covered with tiny white flowers, that feels, in retrospect, quintessentially '90s. And a pair of black platform boots, one of which a boy called Trevor Hackett will piss in.

I go with Mrs Brennan to the dinner, and give a speech that consists of a joke with a hacky punchline that I looked up somewhere, about a duchess being pregnant, that is probably more ribald than they were expecting. But everyone laughs, they are generous. Afterwards, I see my photo in the paper and feel a sensation that will become familiar. In my head that night, I looked sophisticated and pretty, dark haired, dark eyed, winsome – Winona in her black dress at a premiere. The photo shows a stumpy girl with a thatch of bushy hair, red cheeks and a smile that says, please like me. I look good natured, chubby. Provincial. Mammy rings the *Examiner* office for several copies of the photograph. She gives one to Mrs Brennan. She and I beam out from one side of the photo, the good men of the Speakers Club ranged all around us. It could have been worse, the poor boy who won the senior section was spotty, and, at the age of 17, as lanky and awkward as de Valera.

Now we're sitting at the front of the church, right next to the altar. My Dad and my uncles are all in black suits, I don't know where they got them. I'm out on the edge of the row, so I can walk out easily. On the altar, I put the reading on the lectern and I use the same voice I put on for public speaking: clear, prepared, fearless.

The Lord is my shepherd; I shall not want.
He makes me lie down in green pastures: he leads me beside
the still waters.

The Cathedral is full: even in the rain, everyone has come out for her. I can't look at Daddy. I'm wearing the dress I bought for the Speakers Club dinner. It seems shorter already. The skin in my arms pimples with cold when I stand on the draughty altar. November. The river would have been freezing.

Daddy got the call late, he was in bed already. We were all asleep, they didn't wake us. Mammy must have been the one who told us everything the next morning. I wish I could remember what she said. I wish I could remember anything. November, Samhain. The month of the dead. A stretch of black cold nights after the plastic bag rustle of trick or treating and before our Christmas revelry. Early evening she went in – it took them a few hours to find a next of kin for her.

She went in by St Mary's, they said, the big wedding cake belonging to the Dominicans, with stone steps up to its rows

64

of classical pillars holding up the vaulted ceiling. We went there with St Angela's for Mass at Easter and Christmas, all stuck together in the middle pews, shivering and giggling. Nana – she was always Nana, never Granny, and her given name was Catherine – died on November 22, a week before the advent candles would start guttering on the altar, pink and purple, colours of waiting and celebration, with their matching crepe paper on an evergreen ring of holly.

She was 66 years old when she left her house that night and walked the few metres to the river. I remember her in skirts always, sturdy tweed constructions that held her solid as the hills outside the city. Gold-rimmed glasses, merry eyes like my father's. Her house squeaked. Lino everywhere, from the front door and up three sets of stairs and landings. Along that part of the quay, there's a heavy metal chain you have to unlock or lift up to get down the slippery stone steps to the water. It's low enough that she might have been able to swing a leg up and over. Two or three steps then, before you reach the water. The river was probably high, it rains constantly in November. And the cold is something else too, the wind that comes along the quays at night has a knife in it.

Someone saw her, a passer-by most likely. There are life preservers, fat red circles, on wooden posts at intervals along the river. I don't think anybody threw one. The Guards, or the ambulance people, whoever it was, got there quickly, which was lucky. The current is fast – some have been swept all the way out to the harbour. I think of her, every time I am walking along the quay, and I see blue lights flashing ahead in the darkness.

A thing to know: I have no memories, none whatsoever, of seeing Nana outside of her house, ever. And even what recollections I have of her in there are patchy. It was my sister who spent time down there. John Paul and I kept our distance – for all our warring with her, we were our mother's children. And the battle lines had been drawn between Mammy and her mother-in-law a long time before we were born. Nana lived in a white house, tall and narrow, that the corporation gave her. Three stories, and a small backyard, one street back from the river, on the Northside of course, in the inner city. She had an inside toilet, after raising twelve children with an outdoor privy. My grandfather sat in his chair upstairs, watching television, and one floor higher lived their eldest son, my uncle, handsome under the red swelling that, as the years went on, mottled his features. He'd gone to sea at 14, Daddy said. He'd brought back a pair of lovebirds one time, I always wanted to see them. I climbed up to his room at the top of the house once, and was beaten back down the stairs by a smell of piss and whiskey suggestive of a more serious order of drinking than even I was familiar with. Nana also lived with my youngest aunt and one of our cousins, who moved in with her around the age of ten. They all slept together, in a big bed on the first landing that I looked at sometimes, wondering what it would be like to cuddle in there. My sister said the sleeps were brilliant.

Downstairs, there was always a thin metal pot boiling on the hob in the kitchen, the old-fashioned kind with two small handles either side and a burnt black bottom. She mashed potatoes and sent me upstairs with a plate of them, heaped high beside sour piles of cabbage and bacon, to my grandfather, who would eat them in front of darts or motor racing or snooker usually. He spent his working life as a docker, in the port of Cork, while she was at home with all of the children. Grumpy was a big man who filled his armchair, one fat white curl of hair on a bald head, minus a thumb and missing a few teeth. He drank two-litre bottles of fizzy drinks and never said much to me. By the time I was five or six, Mammy's disdain for him was already well rooted and well communicated: until I was about 12 I thought the word 'docker' was an insult, not a profession.

The morning after she died, I turned on the radio in the kitchen. 'Turn it off,' Mammy hissed, low and vicious. 'Turn it off! And your Dad upstairs, with his mother down in McAuliffes. Turn it off this minute!' I turned it off, and turned my back on her. I was trying to make everything normal. I knew it wasn't. I was buttering bread, with the spreadable Kerrygold Mammy turned up her nose at. The knife went through the pale yellow butter, crumbs gathering in the grooves of the chopping board, oily smear of butter on the knob of the radio where I touched it. All the ordinary, shabby trappings of a morning. Except it wasn't ordinary. They rang him, she whispered while he slept above us, at 11 o'clock last night, to go and identify the body.

Some strange voice down the line, a Guard with a country accent probably. He'd have picked his jeans off the floor, or his work pants with the busted seams, loose change rattling. Tied his belt. Pushed his feet into the boots he took off earlier. When they got to the mortuary, a mean little building, next to the small Guards station on the other side of the river, Mammy insisted on going in with him. The Guards let her in, she said, because of her nursing training. I don't know if it's true or not, but I like to think of it. 'And all they had over her was a dirty bit of blanket, may God forgive them.' As she said it, her lips twisted. She never forgave that lack of dignity.

Even though I walk through the valley of the shadow of death,
I will fear no evil, for you are with me;
your rod and your staff, they comfort me.

The microphone is very powerful, built for flinging out prayers to hundreds. It is my first time having reverb on my voice and I like it. The reading takes a long time once I get started. I think about the green pastures, and of the little furry sprigs of plastic grass between the pale legs of lamb in the butchers on Shandon Street.

'Very good, Moll,' says my Dad, when I come back down, the heels of my boots clicking businesslike on the marble altar. I look up into his face, the same and changed forever, and suddenly refuse to believe what is happening with all the force in my body. I am clenched with it. Further along the pew, one of his sisters is staring up at the casket, all gleaming brass and wood on the altar. She is from Manchester – it makes death real, people from England coming. She looks like my Dad, curly dark hair, dark eyes, large features, an overall impression of healthy vigour shared by him and all his siblings. 'Perfect teeth, the whole lot of them,' Mammy would say bitterly. Outside the church she comes up to me, grabs my hand and fills it with a fistful of crumpled money. 'For your confirmation.' I smile up stupidly, not wanting to say it was years ago. My brother gets an even bigger haul, having made his more recently.

Mammy tends to Daddy's grief jealously. 'He'll only cry with me,' she'll say solemnly. The love he has for me and my sister especially – simple, lavish, doting – she treats as a provocation. 'I knew him before any of ye!' she shrieks when she catches us gloating over him when he comes in from the High House, eating his chips, emptying out his pockets. How we worship him, with his big dark beard, and the smile that shows his dimples. When we go on holidays to Kerry, after the pub down the village, he sits at the table in the caravan, eyes half closed, blissed out to Charley Pride, Marty Robbins, Don Williams. 'Keep it country,' he says, in a bad American accent, making a gun of his thumb and forefinger, cocking it at us. 'You know there's only two kinds of music – Country, and Western!' I make lists of collective nouns of animals and memorise them to show him. 'Come on Moll, what's that one?' – pointing with his walking stick, the one with the head of an Irish Setter on it, at a raven.

'An unkindness' I say, savouring it. 'Unless it's a crow, in which case, you know it, a murder.'

'Very good, very good Moll.' Digging the stick into the soft ground, leading us on further. Moll Bawn was my name, from where I never knew, some old song or story. Quick to anger, always, with a fat tongue that curled under itself when he was losing it, nature's warning signal. Big hands that are gentle with dogs and cats and all the wild things we come across, a soft aah in his throat when we find a creature that is struggling or broken. My mother says he used to have a ferret in his pocket, back when she met him. 'No no,' he says when I beg for one. 'You couldn't, Moll, they're too dangerous, teeth like needles.' Sarah and I scratch his back, his palms, his head when he lies out on the sofa, watching telly on Saturdays. Mammy resents it – she's the one who minds us, feeds us, cleans the house, all the daily drudgery. But how can she compete? He washes the ware with the Statler Brothers on the record player, does it with such satisfaction, such care, that the whole house seems to sparkle afterwards. And now this thing has happened that none of us have words for. In some strange, incoherent way I am ashamed of him – ashamed it has happened, ashamed for him that he couldn't stop it.

Nine

'If she's that sick, sure she can't come home. Who'll mind her?'
He's not driving fast by any means, just not as slow as usual.
Sarah always says you'd push it faster. 'Imagine if it was the
middle of the night and I was there on my own? What would
I do?' I don't say anything. Therapy is teaching me something.
We pass the sign for Innishannon, green and white with a stylised
fuchsia. In the back, the dog smells of river water.

'It's not looking good, is it?'

'No Daddy. No it isn't.' The river flashes by, trees steepling
over it, carbon-black and leafless.

'I was thinking, I'll get a camper van next summer. We'll do
the Wild Atlantic Way, myself and Tess will.' Her tail thumps the
back seat when she hears her name.

'Mammy says her bed is like the Merries, the way it goes up
and down.'

'Ha! Perks, is it?'

His laugh is something jerked out of him. We only went to the Merries once, all together – at Perks in Youghal. Mammy went on the ghost train with me, uncharacteristically. She was beside me in the tiny car as it lurched forward. Metal doors slamming back with a bang, revealing the black mouth of the tunnel, waves of delighted panic washing over me. Long wisps of white hair brushing across my face, as we rolled along, high-pitched screams going off by my ear, tinny and distorted from the tape recorder. I held on tight, my eyes squeezed shut in the darkness. Her favourite was the two-pence machine – you'd drop them in to push a pile of coins off a tower of platforms that shrunk and lengthened at intervals. She stood in front of it, feeding money in steadily, watching the rhythm intently, rewarded with a gush of coppers eventually. Probably only a fiver's worth, but it looked like a fortune, everyone had to help hold it.

In the hospital earlier, when she sat up, all you could see was an expanse of flat chest where her pyjama top gaped open. Her breasts were gone months ago. She lost most of her body weight overnight, seemingly.

She's fussing over the morphine pump when we get there, trying to sit upright without getting it tangled around her. It's attached to her belly with long grey cords, like she's a toy you plug into a socket. I lift her legs on top of a pillow, feel the knit of bare bones beneath my fingers: two long femurs, the roundy bulge of kneecaps, tibia and fibula, laughably twiggy. Her feet are in bed socks, ice-cream-striped, pink and white and fluffy. The skin on her shins is so white, the top of the socks disappear into them. She smacks her lips, her mouth toothless and flappy. Roman, we always called her nose, but now she's like a bald eagle. She complains that the bedclothes aren't straight, we rearrange them. The pink pyjamas have a cherry blossom pattern on them, vaguely Japanese looking.

Daddy stands at the bottom of the bed, a new clean shirt on, his big-brimmed cowboy hat in his hands, looking terrified.

'You're going down to see that witch from New Zealand, aren't you?' she says to me.

'I am going to West Cork, yes.'

'To see the witch. On her broomstick.'

'Stop calling her that, she's my friend.'

'She's a witch, you know she is. She took you away from me. And here I am in hospital, your sick mother, and you're going off down to West Cork with your Dad, to her, the cheek of you.'

Her gaze, which has been fixed above, like she's watching TV on the ceiling, suddenly swings towards me. Her arm shoots out – an angry purple bruise splashed across the crook of it – and grabs something off the locker. She holds it towards me. A Ziploc bag with a mandarin in it, and two individually wrapped biscuits. I've seen the orderly giving them out with cups of tea.

'Take them. Quick!' Hissing. 'Put them in your pocket before they see you! You stupid fool, come on before they notice. Take them down to West Cork with you, have them with the witch.'

Later on, back at home in New Zealand, I'll see the blue top of the bag peeking out from inside my jacket in one of our last photos.

The woman in the bed opposite starts roaring at the orderly. 'Get away from me, you stupid little fucker! All of ye are useless!' Sarah and I goggle at her discreetly, not wanting to be caught looking. The woman is large, white-haired, distressed, wearing a nightshirt with a koala on it that says 'ME TIME'. Sarah says they only brought her in a few hours earlier. There's a quick ripple of interest around the ward, all the other bird-thin women temporarily energised by the disturbance. But they're too frail to bother for long, they sink back into their own self-absorption. Mammy's bed is beside an open doorway, which feels undefended, given the sudden bursts of noise and violence we've seen already. But she seems happy enough here. She keeps saying she's going home. I don't know where she got that idea, unless she means going home to Jesus.

Daddy picks up my bag, eager to get out into the open. I can feel the anxiety coming in waves off him. 'I'll follow you down,' I say, and he races for the corridor.

I bend and kiss the hectic spot below Mammy's cheekbone. As I lift my face up, my lips graze the bare patch on her temple where a tuft of pink hair is missing. The oncologist is still saying days, but he was saying that two weeks ago. It's Wednesday now, she was meant to be dead already. I've lost all faith in Byrne. Before I leave we take another photo of our hands alongside each other. Still the same, except mine are so much bigger now, and browner. 'I'll see you when I come back on Friday.'

Outside in the corridor, all the nurses have black smears on their foreheads. There's a moment where I feel like I've walked onto the set of some weird horror film or medieval reenactment – they look savage, like they're painted up for battle. Then I see the priest in front of the window. He's on his mobile, in long black robes and a purple surplice, incongruous against the light-industrial backdrop of the hospital, the heart monitors and wheelie walkers. Like a real-life Father Ted. I can't remember the last time I saw a priest in the flesh, just walking around, doing his business. Where I live, you have to go looking for them. Crosses, I realise. They're crosses on the nurses' foreheads. Ash Wednesday. *Knit me, that I am crumbled dust.*

Like anyone in this place needs a reminder of where we're headed.

It's still light when Bridget finishes. We drive to Castlefreke before the jetlag gets me. We're nearly at the top of the hill when the rain comes on, the big Celtic cross looming over us. Black tree stumps rise out of the mist, white-tops ride up the beach at Long Strand far below us. The rain in my mouth has a faint sea-tang. There's a pale light in the highest part of the sky, out over the ocean that makes me think of summer. Up here, it's like John and Eve never happened. I'm 16 years old, going into the second-hand shop on Winthrop Street, Riddled with Gorgeous, trying on tie-dye hippie dresses, and a mutton-sleeve white blouse with flower embroidery. Long strings of love-beads and Winter Dew perfume from The Body Shop. It's light until 10 o'clock every night. I'm listening to Tori Amos and wanting someone, anyone, to kiss me. Anyone who doesn't look like he's going to be robbing cars soon in Knocknaheeny with his brothers and throwing stones at the Number 2 bus.

I wake in the night, in a panic. The toilet gurgles on the other side of the wall. What time is it in New Zealand? She'll be at daycare, singing The Wheels on the Bus, waving starfish hands in the air on the mat with the others. John will have buttoned her cardigan the whole way up so it doesn't get caught in anything, put on her gauzy scarf with the rainbows on it. Of course he won't, it's summer there. Everything there is the polar opposite of what I'm experiencing. I'm too far away, and the wrong way around. Up is down. I squeeze my eyes shut, pull the mohair blanket higher over my shoulders.

Bridget drives expertly through the rain along the narrow roads outside Baltimore. She's been here for more than ten years now, half the year in West Cork, half the year in Hahei when she's lucky. She points at the forest of black pines that were damaged in Storm Ophelia: a giant hand has gouged a long, ragged scratch through them. We walk in the gale to the grey shore at Tralispean, then push through the wind, back up to the car. I'm wearing bright yellow gumboots moulded out of hard plastic, like you'd see in a hospital or an abattoir. My nose is raw, my lips are stinging. The pain in my stomach is at once heavy, and horribly light, like I'm hanging in the air at the top of a roller coaster. We stop for the papers in Baltimore. Bridget says, 'Your face is a funny colour.'

My mouth is full of spit by the time we pull up to the house she has borrowed for us. I go inside and vomit in the toilet of a tidy grey bathroom. My sister texts. Mammy slept well, the nurses told her. They always say that. They'd say that unless she spent the night running up and down the corridor raving.

I sit on the bath and breathe deeply. The panic is in my throat and the top of my chest. There's a faint smell of wood smoke here that's turning my stomach. I wash my hands underneath a large embroidered picture of the lighthouse, framed above the sink. I recognise it – a tea towel we saw in the craft shop down the village in Clonakilty this morning. Whoever lives here is clever with decorating. A big sliding door looks out, all the way over the scrub and rocks to Kerry. The sun's out again, lighting the top of Mount Gabriel.

I feel that clean emptiness that comes after vomiting. The weak relief of it. Mammy is in the Mercy. Dying but not yet dead. I am here, looking down at an upturned boat in Lough Hyne far below me.

'COVID INFECTIONS RISE,' says the front page of *The Guardian*.

Home. Home. I have to go home. Four more days, whether she's dead or not, four more days and I'm going. I won't go earlier, but I'm not staying longer. I don't care about the funeral.

The oncologist texts as I'm getting into bed: Such a difficult time.

Funny choice of words. Difficult is a maths problem, or a crossword puzzle.

Ten

First time. I'm staring into a ring of lights. Little balls of white and orange, twinkling, circling. One, two, three, four, they divide and multiply like cells under a microscope. My stomach heaves, I hang my heavy head down, feel the hot splash on the grass and on my runners. My mouth is full of sweet and sour. 'Ugh, you're after puking. SHE'S AFTER PUKING!' Tina roars down the field to the others, all in various states of sliding, rolling and falling down the ridge of yellow grass between the steps where we hang around every night, and the estate above us. I continue to heave quietly onto my laces. 'Nah, it's all up, it's all up.' Tina is banging my back so hard, her hand is going to go through me. I shamble over to the steps, lie down and lean my head against the cool concrete of the low wall we were sitting on earlier. By my feet is a white plastic bag full of clanking. They only had pint bottles in the off-licence. We'd stared at each other stupidly when the boy came back with them, before Michelle got out her lighter. The cider was warm and too sweet, like the stewed apple Mammy spooned into us as babies. The first few gulps made my lips pucker but after that it was easy. He got us a two-litre of Linden Village as well, for the money. We passed it around after the Bulmers. I don't know when we all started running. The sun was down, but it was still light. We ran down the field, parallel to the blackberry bushes, windmilling our arms in the moth-busy twilight, drunk out of our minds and never more childlike. Then we all went off separately, some of us rolling down the ridge, getting snagged in the young trees the Corporation put in at the start of summer, some of us lying still in the field, hidden by tall grass from the men who passed by taking a shortcut down to The Residence or walking Jack Russells.

Time passes. A year or an hour. It is dark now, the dark of the first stars and cold on my legs. I sit up, staring down the Blarney Road, watching street lights smearing into one another. I pretended I could see my dead dog earlier. 'Sam, Sam!' I shouted into the bushes. 'She sees him, she sees him,' they repeated to each other. Tina said she saw her Nan who died last year, everyone was doing it. At some point, I went back and had the last of the Linden Village. Whatever was at the bottom of the brown plastic bottle was more froth than liquid. I drank it. That was when I started puking. I lie down again, pressing my face against the rough grooves of the brickwork. Why would anyone do this? I didn't even want to go drinking, Mammy had never made it look like anything but trouble. But everyone else wanted to, we were all putting in money. And now here I am seeing lights, imaginary dogs, the world upended. I keep my head on the step until it stops spinning.

When I get up it is even darker, there are only a couple of girls left, the ones whose mams don't care what time they come home. I go over the road fast and light on my feet, racing the buses that come from behind, the drunkenness leaving me. Shouts from the estates up by the reservoir, the occasional orange gleam between houses. The smoke is black and greasy, they must have tyres in the bonfire. When I get home, I go straight up the stairs to the bathroom, and brush my teeth twice watching my reflection carefully. I go in and kiss Daddy, in his bed watching telly. He says 'Jesus, Moll, brush them teeth, your breath is terrible!' I stare at myself again, with the hall light off in the dark bathroom. My eyes are a bit shinier, but my hair is the same, still too big, no matter how much Garnier mousse I put in it. Down in the front room, Mammy is by the fireplace, muttering.

'Don't let that fucking dog out of the utility room!' she screams once, out of nowhere. I close my bedroom door on her.

She isn't drunk every day, but when she's drunk, you know it. 'I've to do my messages' she'll say, getting ready for the bus, or demanding Daddy drop her off somewhere. All my life I've resented this fiction of grocery shopping. Two or three hours, and they're pulling back into the driveway, her smoking defiantly, him seething at having been kept waiting outside the funeral home for ages. On a bad night, he comes back with the seat beside him empty, she spills out of a taxi several hours later. And then, sitting herself at the kitchen table, or next to the fire, settling in for it. No matter where I am in the house, no matter what house I will ever live in, I can hear that pistol crack of a can opening. Carling, Satzenbräu, Tuborg: she never gets any nice drink for herself either.

She never gets tired. That's the thing. Some people, a lot of people, drink and get sleepy. They sink down into it. Mammy is the opposite, it sets off something in her, something that burns and churns with fire unholy. It never matters how many she has to start with, in her little sneaky hole-in-the-walls before she goes to Dunnes for the sliced pans, packets of Penguins, bottles of diluted orange. Stuff that usually ends up flung all over the kitchen or hallway. I don't blame him for that, I don't blame him for anything. I'd fling her messages at her too, if I was big enough. One drink is enough to trip her switch, set it all in motion. The first time I see that cartoon of the scientist drinking from a glowing beaker, changing instantly into something hairy and bulging, it's Mammy I think of.

I don't remember exactly the day I stopped talking to her. It was probably after Bernadette O'Mahony's mother. Mammy rang her one night when I was late coming home and said we were out somewhere on acid. We weren't taking acid, we were 12 at the time, and Bernadette's mother was elderly. I don't know how she got the number, I am careful to keep such things away from her. After that, our communication becomes minimal. I leave notes on the kitchen table, outlining my needs regarding clean clothes, money and school lunches. She writes back, tucking sheets of copybook paper onto the tray with my dinners. They are always full of capitals, and have things in quotation marks that don't need them. 'DON'T PUT "SALT" ON THIS IT HAS SALT ALREADY.' We are all eating in our bedrooms by now – we take her food and deny her the satisfaction of seeing us enjoy it. She presides over her kitchen with martyred tyranny, cooking separate meals on demand. Chicken for me, the almost-vegetarian. Big red bowls of jelly and raspberry ripple ice cream for my brothers. Her cooking is terrible. We love it. And so she keeps all of us from learning anything that might emancipate us from her hold on us. Later I'll watch one of my brothers trying to butter bread after he moved out for university. Nobody has told him you have to take the butter out of the fridge to soften it. Seven slices, one after the other.

•

I open my eyes. The pain is all over my body and the exact centre of my forehead is splitting open. The room is dark, except for a narrow band of light coming under a door in a place I'm not used to. My bed, too, is facing a different way. I'm at Jennifer's, this is the bedroom she shares with her sister. Bits of the night come back in jumbled order, the give of my shoe breaking, my leg buckling under it, the sudden lightness of my body falling sideways. The low thud of bass deep in my stomach. I took a table down with me, next to the DJ box, Jennifer says later. The bouncers came over. There are little glass splinters in my palm, I can feel without looking. Gorbys. Kim must have got us in. I go to pull the covers up over my naked shoulder, and moan as I snag my nails on the blanket. In the light, they're ripped off mostly. One or two torn down so far there's a crust of blood on the cuticle; rinds of black on the ones that have any length in them. That's the most shocking thing, somehow, the sight of those ragged nails I have torn off my fingers and dirtied with no memory of doing it. My legs and arms are covered in strange bruises, bracelets of finger and thumb prints under my shoulders where people tried to catch me, small cuts from the glass, and the mark of a metal drain cover crosshatched on one knee like an etching.

'You fell going in downstairs,' Jennifer says. 'We couldn't carry you any more after we got out of the taxi.' I couldn't hold it against her. They would have been drunk too, it would have been like trying to lift a dead body.

I lie in the dark, trying to remember how it started. Vodka. On top of the press in the front room. Jennifer's mother's, brought back on the ferry from Swansea. An unfamiliar Russian label, not Smirnoff like Mammy and Carmel had. Some of the liquid had congealed around the neck of the bottle and had tiny bits of fluff on it. The cap had been lost for as long as anyone could remember. We had it with orange juice – the smell was so strong it hung on the rim of the glass like smoke, or oil on water. Maybe it was gone off, like they said afterwards, or maybe I just had more than the others.

'Your tits were out,' Jennifer says flatly. The dress I was wearing was green crushed velvet. Square across the chest. Two thin straps. One of them hangs loose, threads trailing where it's been ripped from its stitching. 'Kim tried to cover you. That's when you broke her shoe and pulled the table down on top of us.' The strappy platforms she got for her Christmas outfit are mangled in the downstairs bathroom. Covered in nightclub grime, one on its side, the heel cracked off at a weird angle, a broken message from somewhere I couldn't remember having visited. 'You tried to get off with Ger as well.' Ger is Kim's boyfriend, older, nice to us in a distant sort of way, untouchable.

At some stage in the afternoon, I get up and drag myself downstairs for a shower. When I vomit afterwards, the liquid is chemical and stringy. I feel poisoned in the deepest, softest parts of my body. There's something inevitable about this sensation of ruination – like it has been waiting for me, like I already know this dirty feeling intimately. I try to eat the toast Jennifer's mother makes for me. She's glueing the heel of the shoe and has sewn up the strap of my dress already. She was away last night – Jennifer told her I had three vodkas and it didn't suit me. I don't say anything to Kim about the shoes or about Ger, not even sorry.

At home, nobody notices anything different about me. I stand in the bath, with the little electric shower unit blaring. I poach myself under the water until I am red and steaming. The heat opens the gashes on my knees, thin warm streams of blood flowing down to my ankles. I stick plasters across them, and on my broken nails. I have school in the morning. My stomach is tight and continues to convulse emptily. Behind my nose and the back of my throat are still throbbing from some kind of chemical incursion. I've put something bad in myself and I don't know how long it will take to leave me. Every time I shut my eyes, there's the red light of the club, the arc of my body falling sideways off its seat, pulling the low table of drinks down with me. Jennifer saying 'And then you tried to get off with Ger'. No expression on her face, and she won't look at me when she says it. I get into bed and pull up the duvet, trapping the vodka stink around me.

•

There is a night at my school, nothing formal, just some kind of ice-breaker for parents. It's 5 o'clock and she's hanging drunk already. Her eyes have that weird, unfocused look I especially hate and she's slurring.

'You're not going up there.'

'Watch and see, girl, I'll be fabulous.' She holds the coat up, a big gingery clot of fur that smells like mould and wet animal. She's picked it up in some second-hand place, one of the junk shops she slips into. 'I'm going up there now, I'll be done up massive. I'll be FABULOUS.'

In the hall, I launch myself at her, hammering at her arms, the sides of her slack, drunk face, any part of her I can connect with.

'You're not going up there! You're DRUNK. You're not going anywhere, you're a fucking DISGRACE, do you hear me?'

'Ha!' There's spit on her lip and her fringe is flat to her forehead. 'Just you watch me.' Her mouth is twisted, and when she wipes it there's a long scratch up her arm, bright pink against her freckles.

'You're NOT.' I jump on the coat, puddled on the floor, and tear through the lining at the back of it, big long hissing rips. I crouch low down over it, like I am disembowelling something.

She shrieks, 'Get off it! Get off it! My coat!' Coming at me, her hands in claws. I put my head down and keep ripping, ripping, imagining her, falling out of a taxi in front of the school gates, all the other parents, all my teachers seeing. I let go of the coat, run to the front door, drop the lock and sit in front of it.

'You're not going out.' I am breathless, my heart pounding.

'Don't be so stupid, girl,' she laughs in my face. We both know the back door is open.

There is a moment now, only a moment, when I look to God for help, or anyone. Watch the mad light in her hazel eyes, face vacant otherwise. Look at her and feel such a terrible wave of self-pity that every bone in my body aches with it. This is my mother. This is what she is doing to me. There is nobody to fix this. Nobody is coming. I look at her standing in front of me, swaying slightly, waiting for the next move, and I roll away from the front door. She'll go if she's going. She'll go, and everyone will know and the shame will kill me. I go upstairs and my bedroom is as calm as ever. I want to tear the Athena posters off my walls, punch the glass out of the windows, shred the pillows. I lie on the bed, the tips of my fingers still tingling from hitting her. She stays in the front room all night, I never hear the front door open. The coat sits in its green plastic bag in her bedroom, until I pull it out years later. I have a fancy dress party and wonder if I could use it. But it smells of wet and mould and looks like a dead thing in my hands, the rips in the lining gaping open.

Eleven

I have nothing to do, and it doesn't matter. Eason's is open. I stand in front of all the Point Horrors I've read already. Upstairs to the stationery. If this was a Saturday, we'd be robbing – dropping pens and notebooks into open bags and jacket pockets. We've got so good, Bernadette has to tell her dad someone's mother worked at a pencil factory. Jennifer is reckless, she'll take whole sets: copies, rulers, pencil cases. She got a family-size bag of crisps from Marks and Spencer and walked around pretending to eat them, filling up with German fine-tips, the expensive ones. We wiped the grease off them. But I'm not taking anything in my school uniform, I'm not stupid. It's just somewhere to go to kill time until first class is over.

I don't know when I started coming in late. I'll say I have the dentist, the doctor, a flat tyre on my Dad's car. They never ask for a note if you do it infrequently. And it's a different teacher every morning, you can do it every couple of weeks if you're careful. If it's a double class, you don't have to be in there until 10.30. It isn't like I have anyone to meet even, none of the girls I'm friends with go on the hop, we are all too geeky. I don't know what even comes over me the first time I do it. I just get off the bus and turn to face town instead of the river. Nobody says anything, the teacher must not have noticed. That was the beginning.

As the weeks go by, my last year of secondary school, the pockets of time taken this way become more meaningful to me. I am a good girl, an excellent student. I've already chosen my university course by the start of Sixth Year. Arts at the university down the road from me. 'Only arts' is how we say it, mocking ourselves for not going for law or commerce or dentistry. English and History are my subjects. The points are low this year for entry. It doesn't make any difference to my diligence. I study because I enjoy it, writing endless revision essays on Bolshevism, glaciers, the political evolution of Michael Collins, Handel's Water Music blaring on my cassette deck, bedroom door locked, Mammy on the other side of it, barely audible. She talks and talks and screams and roars, and I ignore her. I know more than she does, about history, about geography, about everything. I know about love now too. I have a boyfriend.

His mother's car is a toy-size Fiat, the next model down from a Bambina. It is mutually arranged that he will park across from the bottom of our estate, next to the upholsterers. I run down there to meet him. I am wearing tight jeans, a stripy cardigan with a V neck, a thin silver chain and rip-off Rouge Noir nail varnish. I am as sexy as I will ever be. My new hips are narrow, my soft belly doesn't bulge like it used to. I look with wonder on this body, waiting for the day it will leave me. My boyfriend has sharp cheekbones and long dark hair tied back in a low ponytail like Johnny Depp. He wears black jeans and a t-shirt with Kurt Cobain's face on it, tinted purple. He is beautiful rather than handsome, like a Saint or a boy-toy in a Caravaggio painting. We met in a dark little college pub that serves done-up schoolgirls. They play Suede and REM and Blur, you can get cheap vodka and limes and bottles of Bulmers. There's a mural on the wall as you walk in, a cartoon of a man and a woman with cool hair talking about killing her parents and hitting the road, that I only find out twenty years later is a Sonic Youth album cover.

When he kisses me I feel it all over my body. He brushes my cheek with adoring fingers while we are watching *Jurassic Park* on the sofa and I close my eyes in shuddering ecstasy, his small brother sitting on the floor next to us. We touch each other, mostly in the front seats of the tiny car, at the top of rutted lanes down dark boreens selected for this purpose. He reclines my seat and lies on top of me, asking permission for every move. I grant it gravely, swallowing, my voice froggy with wanting. He has learnt to play Metallica songs on the piano, which I try not to notice, ditto that he and his father seem to share a passion for Volvos. The dad is some kind of high-up teacher, a deputy headmaster maybe, at a school near where he lives. I am driven out to meet them, the dad, and the mother, in their big beige house with a sloping driveway and decorative benches in the stepped front garden out in the country. All of the rads are on, and they have a conservatory. Nothing is said about where I am from, or what my parents do, only that I go to St Angela's, a known quantity. His mother has his dark eyes, his narrow wrists, and her own brand of switched-on-ness. She smiles and looks at me carefully. I am welcome in their house after that, and any time my boyfriend reaches for my hand or slips an arm around me, she says sweetly, 'Come on now, don't be pawing her.' Mostly that stops him, but sometimes he just puts it down lower.

We finally have sex on a trip to Dingle, in the westernmost reaches of County Kerry. We'd done our Leaving Cert the week before, all of us, this trip was to celebrate. Are you sure this is OK, he says beforehand, like, when he's on top of me. I think he's trying to be chivalrous. A flash of irritation comes over me, the impulse to say no, actually, let's not bother. It would have been better if he'd just kept going, more exciting somehow. He's so polite and careful. But that's also what I like about him, he is in thrall to me. He's only brought one condom, so when we want to do it again the next night, our only recourse is a pack of three from the dispenser in the pub toilets. It's unknowable whether they were made from inferior rubber, or if it tore as a consequence of tent athletics. All I hear is 'oh fuck' and 'oh God I'm so sorry'.

The next morning, I swing into action. There is no way in hell I am getting pregnant. I'd intended to lose my virginity and go to university, in that order. That was the plan, no variation necessary. I walk him down to the chemist, make him go in. He comes back distraught: they stared at him blankly, and pointed next door to the doctor's surgery. It's one of those pretty, low stone buildings the Americans go nuts for. The gold plaque on the wall is full of Irish names with lots of fadas. I start to realise this might be complicated. When I say why we're there, the receptionist drops her smile abruptly.

I have been practising in the waiting room, racking my brain for the right construction. 'Tá emergency contraception uaim.' This was not one of the scenarios covered in my Irish oral exam a few weeks previously. The doctor understands me well enough, though. He gives my boyfriend a lecture on 'getting a girl into this condition' and tells me I might get sick as if I deserve to. But he writes a script in the end, flings it across the desk to us, looks at me again with his cold little eyes, nods his head, dismisses me.

We give them 50 pounds, the robbers, and I run into the chemist as fast as my legs can take me. My boyfriend cried the night before, when it happened. 'I won't let this ruin your life,' he keeps saying over and over. He'd had a few pints in the pub, but in fairness, I think he has some issues around women. The first time I let him put his hands down my pants, he told me, 'I respect you more than I respect my own mother.' I appreciated the sentiment, but I didn't think he needed to bring her into it.

They give me a whole monthly packet of contraceptive pills – a very basic, old-fashioned version of the morning-after pill. After taking them, I'm sick in my stomach and also ravenously hungry. One of our friends has bought a family-size bar of Whole Nut chocolate. I sit at the mouth of the tent and eat the lot of it. I don't throw up, I feel light-headed and dizzy. He sits close beside me for hours, wanting to take me back to Cork, in case we have to go to hospital. But I'm having none of it. I am on my holidays. We have tents, and freedom and naggins of vodka. I don't drink much that night, I'm afraid the pills would come up if I did. It never occurs to us to be anything but grateful to the doctor.

We have already been having sex for months by the time Mammy gets hold of his mother. He won't tell me what actually happened, only 'Mum was scared' and the inevitable 'I think she had a few drinks in her'. There's a well-known pub in his village, Mammy and Carmel made a day of it. His mum drove her home afterwards, which spared some poor taxi driver. I go cold all over when he tells me. I have my hand on the door of the car, and my vision swims: everything turns into circles and triangles. He keeps talking, swearing his mother didn't think any less of me. And I am just sitting there, I can't say anything. I am thinking, how many days ago? Two, or three? His mother didn't tell him immediately. Has Mammy been up there, sitting in the front room, staring out the window all this time, waiting for me to find out, waiting for me to confront her? I'm not worried about what will happen to me and my boyfriend – in a weird sort of way, it only makes him more mad about me. He loves the way I cry on him sometimes, standing by the river, waiting for a taxi after Friday night vodkas, crying out all my sadness over my mad mother.

I leave the house, go to our friend's place, his parents are on holiday. I take a bag, my boyfriend drives me. I ring my sister, she says Mammy and Daddy are going into my room every night separately, before they go to bed, just standing there looking out the window. Like the parents of a child who'd been murdered. I think 'Good enough for them'. I come back eventually. Everyone except me thinks it's funny. From the get-go, they've had contempt for my boyfriend, his delicate features and fidgety manner. He talks too fast from nervousness, even to my 10-year-old brother. 'He's only an old man anyway.' 'He looks like Granda.' And 'Mammy gave him something to be scared of, ahahaha'. That one is still a punchline.

'She wanted to know if you were on the pill, that's what she was asking my mother,' he says to me in the pub one night, drunkenly solemn at the awfulness of her. I've known in the back of my mind, that's what it must be. She slipped a note under my door months earlier, on the thin white paper she uses for writing letters to our teachers:

'If you're having SEX PLEASE MAKE AN APPOINT-MENT TO SEE DR. COFFEY.'

Dashes through the f's and a curly y like a schoolgirl. I tore that note into ribbons. I can't even remember if I was on the pill by then or not, that's how easy it was to get it.

•

The dress rides too far up my thighs, I pull at it fruitlessly. I'm sitting on an ice-cream fridge, systematically working through a naggin of vodka. Ian tops me up from the carton of orange juice he has in the fridge behind the counter. Ian's shop is a hole-in-the-wall belonging to his mother. People who live on the road come to get cigarettes and papers, a few slices of corned beef, a pound of butter. He lets a few of us hang around here, to talk to, while he stands by the meat slicer, or scoops up 50 pence worth of jellies into plastic bags behind the front window, the kids outside pointing out cola bottles and dolphins. Ian is college age, if he went, which he doesn't. He knows a lot about a lot of things, we spend hours talking about which Smiths album is the best, and casting our fantasy film versions of *The Secret History*.

'Gwyneth for Camilla, we said, the last time, definitely,' Ian says, counting them off on his fingers. 'And what about Christian Slater for Richard?'

I nod, a bit drunk already. 'Christian Slater – yes, that's brilliant.'

'And what about – this might be a bit mad I know – but what about . . . Julian Sands, for Julian?' His eyes are bright behind his round glasses. Ian has a big wide face and coarse dark hair. Privately I think he looks like Morrissey. There's something delicate in how he moves that intensifies the resemblance, but we have never discussed his sexuality.

'No, no, I love it. With the ponytail? From *Highlander*, isn't he?'

'No, that's Christopher Lambert. *Room with a View*, remember, in the field with Helena Bonham Carter?'

'Oh yes. The blond English fella. I can see him as Julian. Totally elegant and sinister. Can I have some more orange juice, Ian?' Am I slurring?

He fills up my drink, which is in a plastic Coke bottle. There's a party tonight, at my boyfriend's school, not a formal dance or anything, just a class bender at a pub up by the university. I'm nervous. Private school boys, loads of them. The dress I'm wearing is Jennifer's, which is why it is too short for me. Another of her mother's specials – black, silky, embossed fabric, with a little keyhole at the breastbone and a Chinese collar. My hair is pulled back and I am wearing a lot of Rimmel Oatmeal Beige foundation. I hope I look elegant.

I finish the naggin and totter into the city. By the time I get there, I've ripped one of the seams on the dress and the slit in the thigh is even higher.

I hear the phone ringing at the bottom of the stairs. My dad's voice calling me. I lever myself off my elbow – my head is actually splitting. Were they up last night? Did he see me? The clock on the table is facing away, but by the amount of light coming in the curtains, I think it's evening. I wiggle out of what's left of the Chinese dress that I slept in. There's something on the front that smells sweet and feels sticky. Orange juice. The smell of it makes my stomach lift. I put on a dressing gown. The action of moving makes me want to faint, or vomit. I hang onto the bannister going down the stairs like a toddler. The door to the front room is closed and the house is quiet. Daddy's gone out, I heard the car leaving. Mammy might be lying down, my sister is somewhere. My brother will be in the front room on his own, watching The Bill omnibus and drinking a three-litre bottle of fizzy apple, his preferred way to spend a Sunday evening. 'Hello?' I croak. I sound like I've been dug up recently.

'Hi.' My boyfriend, sounding tragic already. 'Are you OK?'

'Yeah, yeah. I'm grand. Did you, did you bring me home?'

'Yeah. In a taxi. I brought you up to bed, your Dad left the front door open.'

A silence. It stretches out. I can't remember anything. Flashes maybe. A place with a high roof, the evening light streaming in the windows. Sitting in a long row of people I didn't know, getting up again. Bar stools, low to the ground, with dark-blue upholstery. Little quarters of lemon and the Saxa salt shaker. My stomach heaves. Tequila.

'Do you love him?' he's saying.

'What?' I'm trying to tune back in, I wasn't listening.

'Do you love him?' Choked and anguished.

'Love who?'

'Sean.'

'Sean? Who's Sean?' I see him now, a happy-faced boy with John Lennon glasses. One of the few guys I knew from that school, worked in a cafe in town on Saturdays, friendly to everybody. 'Why would I love Sean? What do you mean?' I'm genuinely confused, I barely know him.

'You were sitting on his lap, stroking his tie, you said you liked it.' Flash of yellow paisley. Those stupid fucking ties they were all wearing. 'Did you get off with him?'

More nausea. Jesus Christ, I hope not. I could have. No memory whatsoever. 'No! Jesus, of course I didn't. I would never. I don't even . . .' Raising my voice is a misjudgement, my head starts pounding.

'Well, what am I supposed to think, Noelle? You were sitting on his lap, flirting with him, in front of everyone.'

'I'm sorry. I don't remember.'

'And then you got sick all over the Ladies. I had to go in and get you.'

I'm looking down at my nails in wonder. They're black again, deep along the nail bed, dirt that once again I have no memory of acquiring. I am thinking of my body, my arms, my legs, travelling through space and time unpiloted. Sitting on Sean, lying in the bathrooms, poured into a taxi later.

'Just once you're OK, I was worried. I thought you might get sick in the night . . . I didn't want to ring and get you into trouble.'

'I'm fine, I'm fine. I was locked, I had a whole naggin before I came in, I was stupid. I love you, I don't love Sean, I don't even know him. I'm sorry, I'm sorry.' I'm too dehydrated to cry, but I want to throw myself in a lake of shame and drown in it.

'It's all right, I'm glad you're all right.' He sounds so sad I am flayed open.

'I am, I am. Thank you for looking after me,' I say – grateful, shaking, knowing I got away with it.

Twelve

Going up the hill, I watch my feet, in open-front black wedges I bought with the money from waitressing all summer. My lilac toes wink up at me. Oasis are playing Páirc Uí Chaoimh tonight, the timing couldn't be better. The rip in my jeans stretches across the top of my thigh pleasantly. It's my first and last time going up to school not in my uniform. My hair is tied back except for two long tendrils, one either side of my forehead. My choker is a thin strip of black leather with a little silver heart in the centre. In the shadowy coolness of the hallway outside the library, I stand in a line with some of the girls from my year. I don't know when I'll see them again after today. The thought is energising. One by one, we're brought into the library where the head mistress is waiting. I walk towards her, she holds out a thin sheet of yellow paper.

'Five A1s and two A2s' I tell Mammy, from the payphone across from the secretary's office. 'I don't know what happened with History.'

'Oh Noelle, thank God and his Blessed Mother! Sure they did the novena!'

'It's not the fucking priests Mam, I studied.'

'Ah there's great power in faith Noelle! He never lets you down, St Joseph of Cupertino.'

Mammy has a job now, in the evenings, looking after elderly priests. They are all put up together by their order, in a house on the Blackrock Road, when they come back from their missions in Africa or wherever, palsied with malaria. She sits with them, and talks to them, brings tiny bottles of whiskey for her favourites. They pray for all of us – me, John Paul and Sarah – for the Junior Certificate, and then the Leaving.

'You've a beautiful mind Noelle, God bless you. Well done, girl. Go on away for yourself, so, and celebrate.'

Daddy looks at me sideways a few weeks later when he realises I have enough Leaving Cert points to do law or medicine instead. Something passes over his face – disappointment, maybe, or exasperation – but he says, 'Sure I don't care what you do, once you're happy.'

College is my first student ID card – laminated, thrillingly. Rows of bent heads under bright lights in basement lectures. Anglo-Saxon poetry, guttural-sounding and wizardy, shouted out suddenly by a white-haired professor, first thing on a rainy Monday. *Beowulf, The Dream of the Rood*, wet coats steaming all around me. Counting all the other left-handers. Walking out in the evenings, past piles of freshers' week fliers tangled up with orange leaves in the automatic doors of the library. Through the quadrangle, sitting neatly, serenely in the grey stone elegance of the nineteenth century. Down along to the river where Daddy waits, cursing the traffic. My first essay, on Sophocles'

Oedipus Rex, comes back with a note in the margin: 'Avoid foregrounding the subjective.' I give John Paul the Louder than Bombs CD somebody recommends to me. A few nights later he comes into my room and says solemnly, 'You were right about Morrissey.' We play Cemetry Gates again and again. Mammy leaves my washing in a neat pile at the end of my bed. I see her rarely.

Second year of university. I carry my college books in a red vinyl bag that says CLUBSTER, go to London for a weekend, get a white ski jacket with a furry hood from Miss Selfridge. I break up with one boyfriend, find another. I meet him at the student club night in town called Gigantic, on a Wednesday. He spills his drink on me. He is wearing a giant black fluffy coat that makes him look like Big Bird, if Big Bird was goth-y. I know his face, all long and chiselled, he works in a pub so cool I'm almost afraid to go into it. He and his workmates all turn up in the clubs together after last orders, moving as a single unit, self-contained and raucous, passing drinks from the bar to the dancefloor over each other's shoulders, shouting and laughing and dancing, cooler than everyone, in their Adidas jackets and Carhartt baggies. The girls have glitter on their eyelids and their hair in raver bunches; the boys are gay, some of them, intimi-datingly dressed, in clothes you can't buy in Cork. They stare at you frankly and keep their backpacks on when they're dancing.

Cork is a young person's city, with club nights and DJs famous all over England and Europe, shops where you can buy Buffalo boots and Duffer jackets, and bars like the one my new boyfriend works at, pulling pints while he does his Masters in Drama. The pub is a big white cavernous space that used to be a warehouse down in Cornmarket Street in the centre of the city. We knew it was taking off when one of the guys from the Happy Mondays started selling drugs there on Sundays. My boyfriend is tall and blond and severely good looking, but his personality is sweet and goofy. He has a hooting laugh and tells Dad jokes already. It's Valentine's Day when we get together properly. He brings me to a party in a seedy old hotel on the quays, that one of his bosses has rented for a club night. The theme is '70s American prom, with pink and baby blue spotlights and paper-chain garlands. The band play disco and funk music in salmon-coloured tuxedos. They're called Sexual Chocolate. It's years before I get that the name's from *Coming to America*, but I love it all anyway. At the end of the night, the DJ plays Moon River and we dance close together. He leans down and kisses me, the pink spotlights playing over us. After that, we're together all the time, for the next few years anyway.

I answer an ad in the paper, for a house share with two music students. Mary and Cait are vegetarians who drink pints of stout, recently back from a drumming field trip in Africa. They make bean chilli and rice for me, that we all eat together, off one big melamine plate on the sitting room floor. Mary says you'd use your hands if we were doing it properly but brings out forks when I look worried. Cait is dark haired and gentle, the first person I've met with a Northern Irish accent. Mary has greeny-blue eyes, a gap between her teeth and incredible stamina. She can stay up all night, and still make her lectures every morning. She knows everyone who makes any kind of music in the city. She tries to teach me how to shake the little seed pods they give babies in Ghana. I have no rhythm, I warn her. She laughs when I prove it. Daddy calls her the drum banger. The drum she plays for her degree performance is so big they have to wheel it out on a little trolley. I sit at the front with a packet of bandages for when her fingers start bleeding. Our house has a bright blue door, with a little pane of glass in a half-moon shape over the knocker. I have the top-floor bedroom, with three big windows. I rent us a television in a shop by the river and get a free mobile phone with it, a big fat thing with buttons that light up when it rings, and an aerial. My boyfriend comes to visit, brings me an orange lily. We go to bed under my new green-and-gold duvet, playing DJ Shadow's Midnight In A Perfect World for hours. He buys *The Guardian* with a student discount, leaves the pages all over my bedroom in the mornings. Mary gets a job in the bar that he works at.

Ruth is my other new friend, from up the country. Her boyfriend works with my boyfriend, we start waitressing together. She moves into our house at some point, the timeline is hazy. Ruth has a fast metabolism and a narrow dancer's body. She wears tight dresses, red mostly, keeps her bedroom extremely tidy and listens to the same Nelly Furtado song on repeat. One summer, we go to Greece together without bringing enough money. 'Tell me a story, Noel,' she says on the beach one morning, the empty day stretching out before us. Sitting beside a deep rockpool, the sun beating down, avoiding a leathery German man with a cock ring, I tell her *Othello*. 'Why didn't he believe her?' she keeps asking. I laugh – 'Because Iago's telling him what a slut she is the whole time, remember.'

Meeting Edel feels inevitable, like the start of every great love does, even though I don't remember it properly. We're in the Half Moon Club, and she's leaning against the bar, or the mirrored wall, or the doorway, arching her back, twisting away from whoever is talking, laughing, with her head thrown back and her mouth open. Beautiful in a way I haven't seen women be, outside of paintings, with a big nose, cat eyes, and a lot of fake tan, this being Ireland in the late '90s. We'd have started out that night at someone's place, where you'd always find at least two of the following cultural artefacts: a poster of a Vincent Van Gogh painting, the soundtrack of *Betty Blue*, a dark, smelly, everlasting lump of hash, and a copy of Toni Morrison's *Beloved*. Maybe it's upstairs we meet properly, up on the navy-blue landing of the Half Moon, next to the cloakroom, shrieking and hugging with the hand dryer in the Ladies going. The DJ's bass coming up through the floorboards. We grip each other's wrists, howling in delight and recognition. We are Absolutely Fabulous from that first instant, one tall and blonde, one small and curly.

My boyfriend isn't happy. They kissed the year before. Some complication, crossed wires, nothing big enough for real bad feeling, but he isn't exactly pleased to see her. A blow-up then, swift and kinetic in the middle of the dancefloor. He throws a drink at her, or I throw one at him. There's always a new kind of drink everyone suddenly starts ordering: Mt Gay and Coke, gin and bitter lemon, expensive, ammoniac combinations. He goes home in the end, and that makes it simpler. We run back to her flat that looks down on the city, turn on the fairy lights and smoke cigarettes out the big sash windows. In my mind, on this night, no matter how much we drink, we stay in that magical sweet spot where you're drunk, but serene, loose and easy. The park, when we reach it, carried on a wave of high spirits from the other end of the city, is green and still in the cool of the morning, the river alongside it brown and sleeping. We creep in at the edge of the water, swinging ourselves down from the railings on the mucky bank of the river. Inside, on the lawns, the roses are still curled up tight, waiting for sunrise.

I go up to Hollymount for my dinner every Sunday: roast beef, lamb, stuffed pork steak from the Shandon Street butchers. Mammy cuts thick slices from the meat bent over the electric carving knife in the corner of the kitchen, the long, thin serrated blades whirring. It was a wedding present I think, the knife – nobody but she is allowed to use it. She makes me sit at the table before the meat is cut, so she can put the plate down in front of me. It's a bad time by then, 2 o'clock on a Sunday. She starts drinking while she's doing the potatoes in the front room late in the morning, dropping them peeled and yellow into the pot of cold water between her knees where she sits on the sofa, a can of whatever next to her. Everything gets tenser and tenser until the dinner's on the table, and then she explodes with some stored-up resentment, and someone tells her to fuck off – me, usually.

'You'd think you'd be a bit more civil, and I doing your dinner. Shit is my thanks, as usual.'

'Think again, Carol.' I fork up a roast potato. They're delicious. She does them in dripping.

One afternoon, I'm in her bedroom after my dinner, going through a box of her old clothes for some reason, when I find a pile of old photos, slightly stuck together and bevelled at the edges like they were in the '70s. She's my age in one of them, around 20. Her hair is short and her eyeshadow is shimmery. She's wearing a white t-shirt, in the middle of a crowd of drinkers. They're all packed in together, underneath a big mirror that says Beamish in black and red and gold ornate writing, all smiling. Kinsale, maybe. They used to go to The Spaniard, I remember her saying. She had friends, is the thought that I have, listening to her downstairs, shouting something at Daddy. She had friends and they liked her. I stare at the photo, the splashy pub upholstery, the amber pints on the table. There's a man next to her, who was he? I recoil from my own curiosity. I put the photos back in the box.

Sarah rings a few days later, to say they're thinking of adopting a Romanian baby.

'Why the fuck would she do that . . . ?' Words fail me.

'But those children might be glad of a family,' my boyfriend says in the bed beside me. I glare at him. 'No, it'll never happen, they won't be able to fill out the papers. It's that she thinks she could be a good mother though, isn't that crazy?'

•

When I wake up, my stomach's already roiling. There's bile in my throat and the room is spinning. In the mirror in the bathroom, I see I'm bruised purple along one side of my body. Creeping back into bed, I can sense he's awake but I don't say anything. Leaning against the cool of his back to quell the nausea, I shut my eyes, willing myself not to vomit.

'Why did you say all that last night, to Paul Horgan?' The words hang there. I don't know what I said, only that I shouldn't have said it. My voice is hoarse from the fags and the vomiting. 'Ah, I didn't mean it. It was 3 o'clock in the morning. He won't remember.'

'He wasn't drunk. You were. We were all working. It was embarrassing.' He turns over to face me.

'He's annoying. I don't like the way he just sits there and stares at everyone.'

'He's the boss, Noelle, he owns the place – he can do what he wants. You can't just be going around spitting at people – not unless you want to be . . . some kind of punk or something!' His voice is rising in frustration.

'I didn't spit at him.' Did I? Jesus.

'Not literally, but telling people to fuck off, for no reason.'

I'm full of dumb fury. Fucking Paul Horgan, with his bushy hair and all his DJ friends from Dublin. What do I care about him? He barely looks at me. I'm glad I said what I said, even though I don't remember. He deserved it. I hate his stupid bar full of posers. I'm sick of this stupid city. I can taste the iron tang of dried blood on my back teeth. I hiccup a sob of self-pity. 'I'm sorry. I was drunk. I'll say sorry to him.'

'No, just leave him alone. He'll be fine, just don't go near him.' He blows out a big sigh. 'You're so angry, Noelle. People don't deserve it.' He puts an arm out then, pulls me towards him.

•

'Of course, the idea would be to move towards a PhD eventually.'

I sit up straight and say 'Mmmmm', the soft consonants humming through my body. The thought of a doctorate is honey in my mouth, and ridiculous also. But Professor Dunne is saying it like an obvious conclusion. Last year, I took his seminar in nineteenth-century Irish Literature, and he agreed to let me write about Bram Stoker. It was the very last essay I wrote, in the last exam of my finals. It was quite short, and mostly about sex; my hand was very tired and my writing was very messy. Some time after graduation, I got a letter: the essay had won a prize. Mammy and Daddy came with me on the train to Dublin. We stood together, about a hundred young people, in a big ballroom with glass doors all along one wall and chandeliers sparkling above us and a former Taoiseach presented us with scrolls and told us we were the future. I came back to Cork and changed my Masters subject. I would do a thesis on the nineteenth-century popular gothic tradition. Professor Dunne, with his clever oval face and soft Wexford accent, would be my supervisor. It feels like a good omen that he has long teeth, which when he smiles are revealed in their entirety.

'Some postgraduate work here first, and then, probably, England.' He steeples his fingers together. My essay was 'radical', he tells me. A radical look at female sexuality. I am not sure how exactly. We talk about the future, we talk about *Dracula* mostly – what all of it means culturally, socially, historically. I quote from it too often, he laughs at me indulgently. I walk out and close his door softly. Beside the stairs, the rain is plastering yellow leaves to the window. One floor down, a cistern gurgles. I close my eyes and see my future rolling out the way he described it to me – the MPhil, a PhD, lecturing, conferences, books even. The feminine uncanny, fictions of unease, technologies of monsters. A whole life, built around it. He believes I can do this. I know it. I feel it. I want this so much I can taste it. I walk down the stairs, full of excitement.

I never write more than a few pages of the thesis.

•

'You can come in for a few lunches and I'll see how useful you are to me, and you can see how useful I am to you. And then if we like it, we can stay together. Sound good?'

She's got that funny, chewy accent that makes some of the vowels very short and others long and flat, but she's been in Cork long enough to pick up the sing-song cadence. She's smiling, a big wide smile that makes her eyes crinkle up at the edges. Her lipstick is very red. And she's naturally tanned, a state unheard of in Ireland. Later on, I'll know the lipstick is Chanel, a shade called Dragon, and she'll leave it in a little silver bowl by the till so we both can use it. For now, I find her intimidating.

She puts her hand in the till and takes out a handful of notes. 'So how many shifts do you think you want?'

'Three or four possibly, depending on the money.'

'OK, Noel. Let's see how we go.'

My friend Stephen got me the trial at Cafe Paradiso – he is always a bit ahead of the rest of us. It is the only vegetarian restaurant in Ireland that is a proper restaurant, with lovely furniture and a wine list, as opposed to a cafe selling rosehip tea and baked potatoes stuffed with lentils. It's been on all the top ten lists, someone came over from *The Guardian* to have lunch there. Bridget owns it with her husband, he is from Cork, she is from New Zealand. The year before they opened, a guy from the *Lonely Planet* came into the cafe where Bridget was working. We have our own vegetarian restaurant, she told him – put it in your book, please. What's it called? he asked. Cafe Paradiso, she said, after a place she liked in Wellington.

She doesn't turn up until the middle of lunch service, and then, there she is, a small woman in a gauzy white dress and expensive-looking blonde hair, walking up the centre of the room suddenly, smiling her crinkly-eyed smile at everyone, talking to everyone in her up-and-down voice, banging a big pink plastic laundry bin full of purple napkins against her belly.

'Hi, you must be Noel.'

'Er, Noelle.'

'Noel.' Beaming at me.

Everything in Paradiso is organic – only natural brands of soap, cola, butter beans. They cook and serve stuff I've never even heard of, let alone eaten. Fennel. Camomile flowers. Harissa. The dining room is blue and yellow, wooden furniture painted navy blue, bright artworks, collages made with the pages of old books, and mosaic mirrors everywhere, long ripples of blue, green and aquamarine. The walls themselves are sky blue, a colour that feels flagrant in Cork, where, as if by some ancient consensus, the inside and outside of every house is painted beige or no colour. The front windows to the restaurant are doors actually, three big glass panes that Bridget pulls open as soon as there's as much as a sliver of sunshine, even in winter when the wind is whipping along the quay. When the customers complain, she says, 'Sure it's good for you, central heating makes you scaly.' And they just laugh, and let her, because she is bold and gorgeous, and no matter how full the tiny blue room is – with lawyers and accountants and academics and actors, all the well-heeled burghers of Cork who come in for sheep's cheese galette, and chickpea timbale – she'll always find them a table. When we're heaving on Saturday nights, people are sent next door to the Wine Cellar, to have a drink while they're waiting. The bar there, long, deep and enveloping, is run by Sheila and her sister, who both look like Norman Bates dressed up as his mother. They reuse the lemon slices in the gin and tonic and sell you boxes of matches that have been struck already.

Bridget goes away for a weekend. I run the dining room in a tight black dress and Dragon lipstick. There's a pen in my hair for writing down phone numbers and crossing out bookings. After service, we drink a lot, but not the good stuff. I lock up carefully. At first, I work three nights, while I am meant to be doing my thesis. Slowly, that fiction grows more see-through. Everyone is leaving – London, San Francisco, Sydney. I don't want to go where everyone is going, and I don't want to go for just a year either. When I think about a future in Cork City, the picture comes up empty. Mammy is a weight around my neck, just the idea of her. I don't have a conscious plan yet, but I'm saving my money. 'Go to New Zealand,' says Bridget. 'What's it like?' 'Like this,' she says, gesturing at the blue walls around us, blond wood tables, big doors you pull open. She is from Tauranga – should I go there? 'Oh no, go to Wellington, it's lovely.' She pulls out a *Rough Guide* from the little bookshelf in the corner, flicks through to the maps at the front, two narrow green islands surrounded by blue water. Aotearoa. I try saying it, my tongue stumbling over the unfamiliar double vowels. Aotearoa. A good place to aim for. I take on an extra Sunday shift in a pub, working for a guy Bridget knows.

●

I'm standing in the queue for the pay phones. Behind me, the towers are burning. It's on every TV screen in the Student Union. When Daddy picks up he says 'Did you see it, Moll? Isn't it desperate?' I twist the cord of the receiver, turn my body back to the bank of televisions. Flames licking the blue sky from the roof of the buildings. I'm calling so he'll come and collect me. I'm staying in Hollymount for the next few weeks, before leaving for Southeast Asia with my new boyfriend. My arm is swollen and tender from the shots I just got at the Student Medical Centre: tetanus, diphtheria, yellow fever. I stand in the line of phones, the air heavy with the familiar, bitter smell of over-brewed coffee, as smoke rises into the beautiful autumn day in America. I've spent five years in or around university – three as an undergrad, a year and a bit tinkering round the edges of a Masters. I tell Professor Dunne I would like a year off, and he says to go with his blessing. He'd go too, he says, if he had the chance – he's always wanted to see New Zealand. I think we both know by now that I'm not a starter for academia.

Halloween night. Bridget's garden is draped in fuzzy cobwebs that glow in the dark, there's a plastic demon with red eyes hanging in the sweetcorn. When Bridget opens the door, she's laughing so hard, I can't make out what she's saying. Something something taxi driver, something flowers. She pulls herself together with an effort. The taxi man got the flowers, and his wife wants to know who's sending them. Oh shit. My feet are cold, I'm still in the doorway. Inside, she pours some wine and we sit down and I laugh and laugh along with her, but I still feel a bit sick about everything.

The flowers are from the guy I was seeing. He sent them to Cafe Paradiso to say sorry for attacking my taxi. He kicked the bonnet of the Toyota that came to pick me up and shouted at the driver. Didn't hit him or anything, but the guy got a terrible fright, God help us, and his heart is not great, the base operator told Bridget. When a big bunch of flowers arrived at Paradiso for me, she sent them to the driver. And now his wife thinks he's having an affair with someone. This is how you know Bridget is a Kiwi. Nobody Irish would send flowers to a man, let alone to a taxi driver.

My last shift in the restaurant is my last night in Ireland. At around 8 o'clock we take a photo – Bridget and me, crouched down behind the serving counter, in front of the coffee machine, clinking flutes of Lindauer and laughing in our red lipstick. My hair is short in the photo, and I am weighed down by the presents she gave me: a greenstone ring and a thick silver bracelet. It has my name engraved on it, and a flaming sun with a smile on his face, the Cafe Paradiso logo. Bridget wears a matching one, so do her sisters and nieces. A few years later, I will lose it in a cinema in Auckland, hungover.

Back at Bridget's, she makes us watch the sequel to *Once Were Warriors*. I'm so drunk, my only recollection of it is Temuera Morrison breaking a pool cue. At the airport that morning, Daddy goes off and comes back with an armful of ham sandwiches – for the flight, he says. I don't even thank him. All I can think of is getting to Bangkok. Years later, back in Ireland, at a table out in her back garden, Bridget says, 'I was so happy when you left. I was afraid for you. Just the way that you were, the drinking.'

'Afraid of what?'

'That you'd die,' she says.

Thirteen

'What did you do?'

'What do you mean?' Laughing. I know exactly what he means.

'Well, you've got us all running now. Not a bad morning's work, Irish!'

He's on TV, the guy on the phone. Famous enough that there's a ripple in every room he walks into. He's not the only one ringing. The *New Zealand Herald* called the newsroom earlier, asking if we could send the audio file over. On my mobile there's a message from a journalist, a real one, from a commercial radio station. They probably want to know if there's anything we're holding back, but everyone was hearing everything that happened this morning in real time, the same as I was.

I go back out to my desk, a messy table with an ancient laptop next to the studio, sit at it, not really knowing what to do with myself. My body is still full of adrenaline. I check my email, there's a note from the host of one of the 7 o'clock current affairs shows on television. WELL DONE!!!!!, it says. How did he get my email? I don't know whether to print it out and blow it up, or just forward it to everyone in the country. I shout for Katie, the Breakfast producer, and she reads it over my shoulder. We fall about laughing, high five each other. Shortly, we'll pack up here and go to her house – me, her, and Camilla the Breakfast host – open a bottle of wine and spend the day in the garden, supplementing the first bottle with trips to the off-licence around the corner. The great thing about being at work every day at 6am is that you can start drinking early. I really need one this morning, I don't know how to process everything. I don't even know why it's such a big deal: it was just some pamphlets. The party said they didn't know about them, and then this morning the Leader of the Opposition said he did when I asked him. He kept going on and on about 'this lousy government', which had us in stitches. He comes on gamely every Thursday. Camilla asked him a while back if a woman should get the benefit for breastfeeding a puppy.

Katie stands in the doorway and and reads a print-out from the *Herald*: 'Talking to Noelle McCarthy on 95bFM Breakfast today, Dr Brash said he met members of the church within the last month when they told him they were fed-up with the Government.' Everyone cheers when she says bFM Breakfast. There's an election next weekend, the first one I've ever taken any notice of, let alone had anything to do with. It's Thursday, 8 September 2005, three years and one month since I arrived in New Zealand.

Life is a series of accidents, happy and otherwise. When I was at Cafe Paradiso, a food writer from New Zealand came in for dinner. She gave me her card, said to make sure to ring her if I ever came to Auckland. The card was bright orange, with a block-print of two white fish. I carried it with me through Thailand and Australia, next to my passport in a flesh-coloured anti-theft wallet. I wrote and asked if I could stay with her, and she said I could sublet her room while she researched food in Italy and Southeast Asia. When I got to Auckland, she picked me up from the airport, her bright red hair glinting in the sunlight, her blue sports car matching the jewelled pinafore she wore. Her housemate gave me the number of a maître d' up the road. A couple of days later, I went in the side door of a white wooden building on Ponsonby Road, and down to the staff changing-room of one of the busiest restaurants in Auckland.

I'm used to working somewhere that can be hard to get into, but this place takes things to another level. In the evenings, the queue at the bar is three deep, even on weeknights. At first I feel anxious for the maître d's doing the seating, but nobody seems to mind – it's part of the experience, talking and laughing along the bar with a drink in front of you, checking out your own reflection in the mirrors, the busboys darting back and forth to the steaming glass washers. The noise is deafening, you can't hear anything. Quickly I learn how to kneel in close when I'm telling the specials, but that first week, my voice is gone by Sunday. The best section to work in is the courtyard, with its tables beneath a big spreading tree; lots of big tippers and no need for shouting. It's prime real estate for peacocks; people can't come in or go out without seeing you.

In Cork, being at Cafe Paradiso was a quiet signal that you were part of Ireland's food cognoscenti. But seeing and being seen is the point of this restaurant: people are tanned, worked out, put together to be looked at. Everyone seems famous. It's the America's Cup and my section is often full of beautiful Italian men with Prada shoes and expensive watches. One day a woman comes in, leading another whose face is swathed in bandages. They sit in the corner sipping the soup of the day – the woman's bandages have a little hole for her mouth, like a mummy. When they come back a few weeks later, the skin on her face is stretched tight like a caul on a baby. Tables full of property developers, actors, people in the music business, generalist chancers, lining up outside the wrought-iron gate at five to midday already. By 5 o'clock, they're flopping back on the blond cane chairs, eyes heavy with drink and exhaustion. Sometimes, you'd push a dessert plate between a pair of colleagues kissing deeply. As spring becomes summer the lunches get bigger.

I work nights and doubles. My day off is tip day: Monday. The envelope is usually full: I'm a good waitress and everyone's great-grandmother is from Dublin. Alexander is the maître d'. He has big brown eyes and shirts with tiny flowers. He makes me mix CDs, full of Dolly Parton and Larry McMurtry, calls me Sister of Mercy. Everyone butchers my accent, but he sounds like Saoirse Ronan when he does it. 'Irish!' the regulars shout, waggling empty bottles. 'Another one, Irish!' After our shifts, I go up the road to the bars on the strip with Kiera, who wears immaculate chocolate-brown lipstick, and fairy lights in her red hair for Christmas. The first place has a German name and a long narrow bar running the length of it. The walls are covered in murals of Marlene Dietrich. There's never any light in there, it's like being underwater. I pash the handsome Scottish bartender in a liquor closet, bottles of Absolut lined up on the shelf above us. They say they'll have to put a tarp down, I fall off my stool so often.

Next door, The Whiskey plays Riders on the Storm and LA Woman. In the daytime, it smells like nighttime when you walk past it. In winter they serve mulled wine from a vat on top of the bar, warm and clove-scented with big sticks of cinnamon.

Now, it's summer and we all sit together, all of the waiters, out in the backroom beside the toilets. The alcove is covered by a fringed black curtain – it looks dramatic and vaguely pornographic every time a new person sticks an arm or a leg or a face through it.

My favourite place in the restaurant is the little room at the top of the building where we iron our shirts in the mornings and evenings. It's quiet up there, except for the dryer spinning, full of teatowels and dishcloths for the kitchen. It's nice and warm, with a proper soft carpet, you could pretend that this is a real house where you're living. Looking down onto Ponsonby Road, everything's different from home; the bus stop signage, people's clothes, dogs even. I'm filled with the strangeness of being in New Zealand. The light too, takes some getting used to, the fuchsia dazzle of bougainvillea on white wooden houses, blinding flashes of sun on water.

I move into a flat with a girl from the restaurant, a done-up villa in Freemans Bay. I get an old mattress from somewhere, drag a couple of wooden pallets up the hill from the back of the New World. Why I don't ask someone to drive me to just buy a bed is beyond me now. Beyond the bedroom window is an undeveloped plot of land, low and scrubby, that's been sold for millions since, probably. A prostitute was found down there one night, someone tells me, battered and crying. At night, the shadows from a big palm tree slash across my duvet, like Freddy Kruger's glove that used to terrify me as a 12-year-old. I lie in bed, watching the dark gather in the corners of the empty plot, wishing I had curtains.

Coming up to the first Christmas in New Zealand, I walk around with a homesickness that is constant and shaming. It will be cold back at home, the pubs dark and heaving. Mammy would be insisting on a Santa letter. 'He won't come if you don't believe!' wagging a finger at me, even when I was 20. 'He sees you when you're sleeping!' Singing it in that fake Shirley Temple voice that made me feel like my mouth was full of metal fillings.

'What sort of creep watches you when you're sleeping anyway?'

'Just wait and see. Might be a bag of coal for you, girl, this year.' The Christmas before I left, there was a little seal pup under the tree for me. Grey fur dusted with white, big limpid eyes, like a real one. When you squeezed him he cried. Wailed rather, a high, thin note of sadness that was weirdly genuine. Mammy would cry in ecstasy when she heard it. 'Listen to him, sure God love us, his heart is broken!'

By December, I'm going out with one of the other waiters. Going home with him after Whiskey Bar anyway. He brings me to his family for Christmas, in a big house in a new development by the sea, somewhere north of the city. In the living room, the windows are floor to ceiling, and there's a telescope, the first one I've seen outside of a film or encyclopaedia. We eat crayfish, milky-white chunks that taste faintly bleachy. On Christmas morning, he gives me a zen garden, a neat square of grey sand with a tiny little rake to comb it, and something oblong and black that looks like a coal scuttle. 'It's a planter . . . for flowers and that,' he says, losing his nerve at my expression. I'm torn between contempt and admiration, that he thinks I'm the kind of person who could grow anything.

One warm night, later than you'd want to serve a big party, a group comes into my section in the courtyard. One of them sits directly under the Robinia tree, his chair pushed out so he's apart from the rest of them. He just sits there for most of dinner, in his good suit, double-breasted, eyes half closed, hair waved back from his face like a matinee idol, the others observing a respectful distance. A few years later, when he's shouting at me on the radio, I remember his lit cigarette, how it burned down low between his fingers until he finally smoked it. The radio interview is about some remarks he's made about an Indian radio station. I accuse him of dog-whistle racism. As an immigrant myself, he says, I should know better than to be asking him such bad-faith questions, but what else can you expect from the media? This and more, on and on for ages. When we're off air he rings me back. 'I can give it, Irish, and I can take it as well,' he shouts, laughing. After he hangs up, I sit at the desk, the adrenaline slowly leaving my body, thinking about how weird it was to be shouted at on the radio by the guy from the courtyard at Prego.

I decide that when I get home to Ireland, I will switch to a journalism Masters. But the only decent postgraduate journalism course, in Dublin, requires work experience. 'Go up to the radio station at the university,' a new bartender at the restaurant tells me. 'They're always taking vollies.' He's been going there for months, helping out with a news and current affairs show. Radio was a thing in the corner of the kitchen in Hollymount – I never thought you could have a job being on it. The following week, I go up to a reception desk in one of the brutalist blocks at the University of Auckland, get a photocopied form, fill it out on a sagging leather sofa. Behind the reception desk is a big poster. A red letter b in a white box with black outlines, that looks like a child drew it. YOU LUCKY LITTLE BASTARDS, it says under it.

A week later, I'm at the back door of the station, ringing the buzzer at 5 o'clock in the morning. There's music thumping through the soles of my feet. Through the glass I can see the open door of a toilet cubicle and rows of square shelves lining a dingy-looking corridor. Later I'll see the shelves are full of records. Someone takes me past the studio and into the newsroom – a long plastic desk facing the wall with two early-model desktop computers. Writing news for the breakfast show involves reading a copy of the *New Zealand Herald* and checking the BBC website on a PC with dial-up internet, and writing stories about anything that catches your attention. One morning, the newsreader is away and I step in for her. People like it, the accent – I get more news-reading shifts, despite the fact I have no idea what I'm doing. The day I read MI5 as Em-One-Five in a story about spying and we get complaints is the day I realise I am actually broadcasting and people are listening. I write news before lunch shifts at the restaurant, read news on Drive in the breaks in my doubles.

Not long after I first turn up, I'm brought into a meeting in the boardroom. Would I be willing to go on stage as part of a skit for a music awards thing? One of the girls from Sales is there, smiling at me, she'll be doing it with me. Sure, I say, sounds like a good party, why wouldn't I? On the night, we walk out on stage in a North Shore auditorium, in front of hundreds of people, me and the other woman, both of us dressed in miniskirts, fishnets and leather bustiers. We pull on ropes descending from the top of the stage curtain. The host appears in a harness at the top of the curtain, the Voice of God booms out as we haul him down slowly. He hits the stage, roars into the mic, the signal for general mayhem. Music, cheers, strobe lights. In my memory, there were fireworks, but I know that's an exaggeration. Standing on stage, up above everyone in the high-heeled boots I bought specially, my hair at Diana Ross dimensions with a full can of Elnett, I feel excited, turned on, in my element. I want whatever's going to happen next to happen already. I can't remember the rest of the night, I know I kept that outfit on. I might have slept in it.

I get a trial on the afternoon current affairs show. My hands are shaking so hard, someone else has to cue up a CD for me. The disc has a picture of pink latex hotpants on it, and PROPERTY OF bFM written across the crotch in black marker. I press the icon that says WIRE STING on the studio computer, wait for ten seconds as directed, then pull the channel fader down at the same time as I hit the MIC button. The big red ON AIR light goes on above the notice board full of tattered gig posters in the studio.

'95bFM, you're listening to The Wire. I'm Noelle McCarthy.'

My voice feeding back through the cans is deafening, and a little shaky. I imagine it blaring out of the speakers in the Quad downstairs, coming out of car stereos, playing out of radios sitting on kitchen benches. Massive hit of adrenaline. I uncross my legs, put both feet on the floor, lean my body forward and keep talking. I'm alight with the ease of this, the thrill of it, the electric purity. I go through the rundown, take a breath and say 'This is Peaches' as I hit play on the CD channel and pull up the fader. Distorted synths and drums thump through the mixing desk, a big slab of wood, slightly sticky to the touch, scored with the initials of generations of DJs.

'Turn your mic off,' someone mouths, pointing at the button. I want to get up and run somewhere, I'm so full of energy. The speakers in the studio are up at full volume, music hitting off the walls, shaking the mics on their brackets. 'Don't forget your radio make-up,' the News Director says one day as I'm walking into the studio, and the penny drops: on radio, you need to be yourself, only better. 'It's so good to hear a natural laugh,' someone tells me. After that I laugh frequently.

Soon I'm told that I am being given the slot regularly. I have no idea why I am getting a radio show, when there are other volunteers who've been here longer than me and have more experience. The process behind on-air appointments is opaque, mysterious. There's only a handful of actual jobs at the station – a lot of behind-the-scenes work and most of the on-air shows are done by volunteer DJs. Not a lot of women have paying jobs, that I can see, at this point, apart from a few in Sales and Marketing and the Breakfast producer. There's jokes about Vollie Shags; I don't know if I want to be one or have one. Everyone there is attractive to me – proximity to a microphone makes people sexy. The boys on the TV show *Eating Media Lunch* come in periodically. I'm delighted when they talk to me. Someone says they got thrown out of a press conference for *Lord of the Rings* recently, when one of them stood up and asked Viggo Mortenson if he was enjoying having sex with New Zealand women.

When the News Director leaves, I replace him. The job involves running the volunteers who write and read the news and do the current affairs shows in the afternoons. It comes with an ancient laptop. The money is less than what I got waitressing. After a few weeks a boxful of cards turns up on my desk, with the red b logo and my name and title: Noelle McCarthy, News and Editorial Director. I sit there with the cards in my hands, splaying them out on the desk in front of me.

•

In the second week of December that year, I sit in the middle seat in the middle aisle of two KLM planes, one after the other, for an endless time until we land in Schiphol in the early hours of a day that's already happened in New Zealand. I have not told anyone I am coming. In Cork, Mammy is the same and I am out of practice. Forty-eight hours into it, I hear myself saying 'The next time I come home, it'll be to bury you'. It's like everything that's happened, the life I'm making in New Zealand, none of it exists here. I'm 14 years old again, in my pale green bedroom at the top of the stairs, full of rage and nowhere to take it. On Christmas Day, I lock my bedroom door at 2 o'clock and drink a bottle of Jameson. My dinner congeals on the Ninja Turtles tray out on the landing. The next morning, I walk down to Fitzgerald's Park with my Discman and a CD that Alexander made for me. I listen to the same Whiskeytown song on a loop. The Shakey Bridge, hanging over the river, bounces under my feet lightly, just like it did when we were children. Down in the park, the rose bushes Edel and I ran past years earlier are black and bare, dripping with water. The cold goes up through the soles of my boots, just the way I remember it. I'm planning my funeral: I'll have two, one here, one in New Zealand. Everyone will come. If I die in Auckland, my picture may be in the paper. I hope they use a good one.

Back up at Hollymount Mammy leaves another plate of food outside my door. I shout downstairs that I don't want it. Sarah says, stop drawing her on you, and cop on Noelle, with the whiskey. Three years I was gone, and I don't spend any time with my sister this Christmas. I don't see Robert either. Is John Paul even there? That night, there's a tsunami in Southeast Asia. I say I have to go back to work early – as though coverage of a major international disaster depends on Auckland student radio. Back in New Zealand, jetlagged out of my senses, I'm stopped by a Customs Officer who pulls a mandarin out of my handbag. She lets me off the fine when I start crying. I feel smug later, reading out a news story on Breakfast about how Hilary Swank got caught with an apple and had to pay 200 dollars. At home I sit down with an ice tray and a bottle of duty-free vodka, and breathe out for the first time in ages.

·

The sound of bFM, now and forever, is the opening riff of Seven Nation Army. There's a Christmas tree up for most of the year out at reception, hung with little cut-out photocopied pictures of Jack White and the guy from Queens of the Stone Age. A prize cupboard full of party pills that gets raided periodically.

A guy who sells them comes up for interviews on the breakfast show some mornings, an intense person with big eyes, in a shirt with a Chairman Mao collar. He makes us sign a liability release on air before giving us a dose of the latest versions. I can't remember what they were like, but we survived it. Free bagels, burgers and ice cream when Breakfast and Drive get sponsorship. Names on the door for gigs at Galatos and the St James, but no plus ones unless the rep really likes you. The playlist is programmed manually by a man with pale skin who has the catalogue number for Raw Power tattooed on the inside of his arm and wears black suede brothel creepers. He sits by the door to the studio, blowing air through his long dyed fringe, jumping up, outraged if he suspects a song from the list has been deleted. Everyone up there takes music very fucking seriously. For a while I think they are joking, and then I realise they aren't. People talk about The Dead C and many, many other bands I've never heard of. It doesn't matter.

Not long after I get my visa sorted, things end with my boyfriend. When I find a flat in Ponsonby, while he is staying at his parents', I borrow the bFM van without asking. There's a new vollie up at the station, Rebecca. I ask if she can drive it. Sure, she says, and when I say it's a stick shift she just starts laughing. She'd made us both tea recently, in the little kitchenette in reception, in two black mugs with red b's on them. I nearly cried when I drank it. Nobody can make tea in this country. She idles in a loading zone outside a junk shop while I run up and down stairs, arms full of all my stuff, calves burning. When I'm done, she backs us out into downtown traffic, swinging the big wheel around effortlessly. She says, 'I got the feeling time was of the essence,' with a smile that says, cut the shit, this is a getaway.

The first time I see my photo in a newspaper, I stare at it until my face starts to break down into pixels and shading.

I sit at the kitchen table in my flat in Ponsonby, inhaling my own image, with a vertiginous kind of feeling that's a mix of shame and elation. I didn't want to smile – I was going for self-contained and confident – but I look like I'm sneering at the photographer. I pore over the photo, marvelling in horror. There's a little bulge of belly above the belt of my dress that I'm distraught over. My flatmates cut me out and put me on the fridge door, where I stand, glowering, until the paper curls up and goes yellow. I send a copy to Ireland, as I send all the photos that come later. I pose whenever I am asked, at fashion shows, lunches, gigs, launches. I'm on the invite list for a lot of stuff that happens in Auckland.

I start doing the weekly interviews with the Prime Minister and the Leader of the Opposition. Helen Clark calls in just after the 8 o'clock news every Monday morning. I hate when she rings in the middle of a song – she's not the kind of person you keep waiting. 'What should I call you, Prime Minister?' I ask the first morning. 'Helen,' she says shortly. Daddy starts paying attention when her name comes up in the Irish papers. I burn him a CD of some of our interviews, but they're full of New Zealand politics, I'm not sure he gets much out of it. When the *Listener* asks to do a profile on me, I am mortified – I haven't done enough to warrant being in there. But I agree to the interview anyway. I'm 26 years old and the main thing about me at this point in my life, is that I will say yes to anything.

•

'Just checking in, did you get home all right? Pull up OK this morning?'

'Oh yeah, I'm totally fine. Well, now I am. Bit touch and go earlier.' I laugh, but my heart is beating fast, standing outside Verona.

'Yeah, I was definitely in the dogbox. Had to sleep in the spare room.' I think, but don't say, this is a good thing – my perfume is very strong. I remember the pub, pokies flashing behind us, brandy and drys all over the table. It was my favourite kind of night, day-drinking that slid into evening. Afterwards, we parked up in Grafton somewhere. I'm surprised he could even drive home later. 'Did you make it in to work?' He mustn't have.

'Nah, it was hard getting up, but I'm better now. Going for a wine actually, hair of the dog etcetera.' It's so important to make sure he knows I won't tell anyone. I want him to know he can trust me, now that it is being tested. With him, with all the rest who come afterwards. Their girlfriends, wives, whatever, would never hear a word of it, I am trustworthy. At what point did that become the priority?

'See you tomorrow.'

'Yeah, see you in there.'

And then I ring my friend and laugh about it. A prize in itself, being wanted.

•

Mornings in the studio, me, Camilla and Katie stretched out over the desk laughing, full of the delirium of hangover. It's two years since I started. I'm still looking over at the box of News Director cards on my desk sometimes, to make sure I'm really doing this. Katie comes to my house in the taxi some mornings, gets me out of bed. She buys the crumbed lasagnes from downstairs when the caff opens, whole bay leaves in the mince cutting your mouth with the sharp edges. The grease makes the paper plates see-through. I stuff one down, trying to soothe my curdled stomach, stumble through the bulletin. Camilla cues up that RTX song, that first guitar line so sweet and pure it sounds like it's from a different song altogether, and then the drums kick in and then the vocal, building up to the raucous shouting chorus and the sun streaming in the big streaky window and I swing around the mic stand and bang my chin on the fuzzy pop sock and the wheel of the broken office chair I'm sitting on catches scrunched-up bits of paper beneath it, from when we had to print out the 7 o'clock headlines because the laptop takes a while to get started. My hair's like Stig of the Dump and I'm sweating white wine under my leopard-print t-shirt – but it doesn't matter, nothing matters. The sun's coming up and we're here together.

•

Summer in Ireland. Mammy is across from me at the kitchen table in Hollymount, Daddy's chops congealing in the frying pan on the hob behind her. The pall of smoke hangs over our heads like ectoplasm at a seance. The cooker doesn't look like it's been cleaned since I left off the back of the tsunami excuse eighteen months ago. The kitchen smells like it always does: sweet and meaty, and the dusty smell of central heating. There's an undertow of dog now. Daddy fitted a washing machine for someone who gave him a puppy. Jenny is a Pomeranian; tiny, leonine, fluffy. Vicious also. Someone drove past and stole her recently. They threw her out of the car again before they got to the bottom of the estate, Sarah said. John Paul loves her, comes in drunk and quotes Allen Ginsberg to her from a respectful distance: 'You were never no locomotive, Jenny, you are a sunflower.' I can hear her padding around on her little paws in the utility room behind us, growling.

'If I'd known you were coming, I'd have made you something.' Mammy is pouting.

She taps the fag resentfully, into the big John Player Blue ashtray they got from a pub somewhere. I can feel the anger rising, the familiar, helpless sense of being wronged by all of them, her especially.

'I was only trying to surprise ye! I thought ye'd be happy.'

'And your dad is very upset, he could have collected you from the airport.'

'Shut up about the fucking airport!' They have been talking about how I got in from the airport ever since I turned up at the front door two hours ago. Why didn't I ring anyone? Say I was coming? How much was the cab? That's robbery. I have just spent 2,000 dollars flying here from New Zealand, and all they care about is the 20 Euro I'd have saved by having Daddy collect me.

'You know he loves doing it for ye. He gets very bad about it.' She's the one who loves it. Going back decades, the airport has always been a superior place to party. Auntie Cay, living in America, provided a lot of opportunity for airport conviviality. Everyone made a day of it – made a night of it also, if they could get away with it. I remember faded photos from childhood, square with thick white margins: Mammy with a feathery haircut, a la *Klute*-era Jane Fonda, Daddy shaggy and bearded, Han and Granda, various uncles, all sitting back in spinning chairs upholstered in nubbly '70s fabric. Great long picture windows along one wall, planes lined up outside. They're all holding glasses with Cork Dry Gin stencilled onto them, cheers-ing the camera, departures boards flashing in the background.

'And staying down at Ruth's house? The cheek of you,' Mammy says flatly.

'Ah sure, Carol, I'll be glad to have her.' Ruth is next to me at the kitchen table, drinking one of Mammy's cans gamely.

I reach down, pick up my cider. It is, I think, the first time I've ever had a drink with Mammy. It feels scary, like being on the edge of something that could tip over any moment. I want a cigarette, but I don't want to give her the satisfaction of asking. Hers are horrible, anyway. Outside, the August evening deepens into a dark-blue twilight. The light is so much softer here.

'Your hair is gone long,' she says eventually. 'You put a colour in it.'

'Just a few highlights,' I say, defensively. It's actually too red, I don't like it. 'I got it done for a TV pilot, we had a stylist.' I'm trying to sound like I think it's funny, but it comes out boastful.

'A stylist? Fuck off, Noelle.' Robert, my youngest brother, glares over. He has a beard now, some complicated, barbered arrangement. When I left, he was wearing a school uniform.

'Yes, a stylist, Robert. To get the look right. It's important.' The TV show went to the wall after a few episodes. They were going for witty repartee, but we weren't funny.

'All of that sounds extremely juvenile Noelle, I'm reading Tolstoy.' He reaches over, takes another can of beer out of the plastic six-pack holder, belches quietly, grins at me. He is handsome, I see suddenly.

The evening goes on. Ruth tries to intervene when Mammy and I start gnawing at one another. 'Keep your mouth shut, you, this is between us,' Mammy says. I grab my handbag and tell Ruth we're going.

We walk out into the cool night, pulling the door closed behind us. The hall carpet is still royal-blue-and-cream paisley, a little patch of muddy fuzz by the front door where Daddy's boots walk over it. Every time I come home, this house is waiting. The Busy Lizzie on the counter, the big statue of Jesus on the table next to the window in the kitchen. He's wearing my 21st birthday pink tiara, a pile of soft toys at his feet. 'Mind the Lord's birds!' she yells whenever I brush against them.

The next day I sit next to Mammy on the sofa, flicking through the magazines I brought home to show her. 'You're like

Han there,' she says, pointing at one where I'm sitting in a deck-chair, with very big sunglasses on and a drink on the grass next to me. I hadn't meant to have the drink in the shot but I forgot about it. 'You're terrible in that one,' considering the second magazine cover, where I'm wearing a red dress, red lipstick and very pale foundation. 'Terrible altogether. Who did that to you? You look like Count Dracula.'

Suddenly she looks at me closely. 'What happened to that?'

'What?'

'Your tooth, you're after cracking it' – gesturing at my mouth with her Major.

'It broke,' I mumble, pulling my top lip down over it. My top right front tooth has a perfect little half-scoop of enamel missing at the bottom.

'How?' she says, not waiting for an answer. 'You fell, did you? Come on, tell the truth and shame the devil! Noelle fell, ahahaha!' Her voice is high and mocking.

'Shut up, I banged it, it broke, it was very painful!' My cheeks are flaming, flashing back to a morning in early summer, not long after I arrived in Auckland. I woke up to the voice of one of the maître d's on my answering machine – I was missing my shift, slept in after a late one. Throwing myself into the shower, I banged my head, hard enough to knock myself out for a few moments. When I came to, I was lying on the tiles, water pounding down on me. I went to work dazed – it was halfway through the day when I noticed my front tooth had a chunk missing. The bottom ones are cracked as well, but at the back where you don't really notice. I keep thinking in a vague kind of way about getting them fixed, but I'm afraid it'll be expensive, and who wants to go to the dentist?

'You'll have to do something about that. I'll ring Declan Canty.'

'No. I'm not going near him, you said he's mental.'

Like many Irish people of her generation, Mammy suffered years of childhood torment at the hands of butchering dentists. By the time she was 40, the only teeth in her head that weren't black were gone already. Her top teeth especially were terrible, in photos she always smiled with her lips together. That my father and all of his brothers and sisters had big white grins, she took as a personal insult. 'Horses' teeth, the whole lot of them,' she'd say. But while I've been away, she has come into the orbit of an inner-city dentist, a man whose personality is sufficiently persuasive to talk her into a series of procedures, involving crowns and bridges and similar. 'He's fantastic, girl, very gentle. He'll give you the numbing gel and everything.' She's already walking over to the phone in the kitchen, looking amid the piles of grease-smeared papers on top of the microwave for the number, dialling the surgery.

'I don't want the gel! I don't want anything.'

'Hello. This is Caroline McCarthy.' The pinched, nasal voice she uses for exchanges with any form of authority. 'Hi Christine, it is it is.' Beaming. 'Listen, my daughter is over, from New Zealand . . . Yes, yes, God bless her!' Winking over at me. 'And she has, er, a small' – another wink – 'a small chip in her front tooth, and I was wondering: would Declan ever be able to . . . I know, I know, sure. And he's so busy . . . Tomorrow? No, that's grand. Grand altogether. See you then, Christine. Thanks very much.'

Twenty-four hours later, I'm in a white room rich with the smell of mouthwash and disinfectant. A man with a high aquiline nose, and cheeks red in the middle in perfect, flaming circles, is filling my mouth with putty. 'Right, grand, grand, we've got it here now, juuust a little push, and we have it, we'll make the shape, see?' Holding up a lump of white stuff at me. Grinning widely. His general attitude is one of cheerful mania. Lots of big smiles and ceaseless talking. I decide I like it, although my head is pounding.

'Right then, another little push now, we'll make sure it sticks, don't want it falling out in New Zealand! Ho ho ho. Sure, what's it like? A brilliant place I'd say, I've always wanted to go. And them All Blacks!' He thrusts his whole face up to mine suddenly. Eyeball to eyeball, the pupils of his eyes are dilated and completely black, like a shark. 'The All Blacks! Sure they're FEARSOME!' His voice is full of the singsong bonhomie of all of the professionals in Cork City – lilting and friendly and all business.

'And Caroline outside. Well I'll tell you, she's been a very brave woman, Caroline, very brave altogether. We've been on a grand journey together, did she tell you?' I gurgle. His full head of hair is grey at the temples, lighter than the black eyebrows that curve up into high arches. The wild light in his eyes is alarming. But the latex-gloved fingers under my top lip are gentle, like she promised they would be.

Mammy is out front in the tiny reception, next to the humming blue fish tank, under a pile of *Hello* magazines. Delivering me into this man's hands was some kind of personal zenith for her, earlier. When he came out to get me, she was practically levitating. 'I'll take care of her, Caroline, don't you worry!' It was funny, hearing someone use her full name – made her sound much younger. They had a relationship, I saw then. She loves him. Professionally, at least, nothing sexual or anything – but weirdly, it seems mutual. 'See you soon,' she cooed at me, with a little wave, all girlish as he led me into the surgery.

'I'll just build it up now. Like a wall, sure.' Declan is holding my front tooth firmly, painting on something. 'I mean, I should have been a builder, if I wanted to make money. Hahaha!' He's filling my mouth with some kind of paste. The grains that fall on my tongue taste chalky. 'How did you do this – a MISADVENTURE, was it? Oh to be young!'

'Mirror, please.' Briskly, to the very subdued nurse beside him. Shows me a tiny circle of enamel.

'See, we're nearly ready?' I nod vigorously, biting back the urge to throw up on him. I need these hands to be out of my mouth already. 'Now we've got a bit of damage to these ones too.' Gentle fingers, smoothing over the cracked bottom teeth. I'd gotten used to the jagged edges, they were almost pleasant to worry at when I was anxious or hungover. 'I'll just file them back for now, and sure, you can come in again if you want to the next time.' He is on me with something whirring before I have time to process. But the whirring is brief, and then, one last wild tug on my front tooth and 'All done, see?' A big mirror in my face, suddenly. The tooth is restored perfectly. No more looking like a Victorian street urchin.

'Look at that now! You're a tiger!' He turns his fingers into claws without warning, pulls his top lip up, exposing long white canines. 'Grrrrrr! And no more opening bottles of Heineken with your teeth either!' Bending his mouth down to gnaw on an imaginary beer bottle.

I laugh shakily. When I stand up, my legs are a bit wobbly.

'I told her, Caroline,' he flutes, flinging the surgery door open, 'no more using those teeth as a bottle opener!'

She jumps up, laughing. Glowing in his radiance. 'I hope you told her, Declan! Sure she's desperate!'

'I did! And you know what you do, with those bottles? You just go like this.' And he grabs the big old white-painted door to his surgery, pulls it open, mimes sticking a beer bottle into the hinges. 'In there, you put it. And' – he wrenches the door back savagely – 'see there! You might break the neck off, but sure, it'll be open, anyway! HAHAHA!'

I look at him, crouched almost double in his light blue smock, slamming the door open and shut for me. Mammy is in stitches next to him. Even the receptionist is laughing. He straightens up, out of breath, gives me a hand to shake. His fingers are warm and dry without the gloves on. 'I'll see you again Noelle, safe home to New Zealand now. Come back soon Caroline, we're not finished with you yet!'

We walk down the twisty old stairs from the surgery. I whisper to Mammy about the tiger face. 'Sure, he's red mad isn't he,' she says happily. And then, out on the street, 'I must go do my messages,' turning her face to the wind, zipping up her thin red anorak. Her hair is not pink yet, it's dark brown still, and tufty. I stand watching, wanting to thank her, but the words aren't coming. She shifts her reusable bag from one hand to another. 'Go on, so, I'll see you. Come up for your dinner with Ruth sure, tomorrow.'

'Mammy,' I say. She turns. I put my hands to my face, turn my fingers into claws, lift my top lip up and shout 'Grrrrrr' at her. 'Grrrrrr,' she shouts back, making a claw with her free hand, peeling her lip back, exposing one shiny, fake, incisor.

Fourteen

Up to the shop at the top of the terrace, a little dairy with a floor covered in sticky linoleum. Out the back, past the overripe bananas, next to the toothpaste and the tampons, there's a small display of cheap wine bottles. Nobody else buys them, or knows they're there even. I've only come for one, but I pick up a second at the last moment, as though I wasn't always going to. I wind my fingers around the green necks of the bottles, clinking them onto the oilcloth counter. I chuck a dollar bag of cola bottles on top as I hand my card over. I always do that – my desk is full of little plastic packets of sun-warmed lollies, as though buying sweets legitimises a wine-run. Twenty dollars for two bottles. There's more expensive ones back there, but why would you? This one tastes like Ribena, goes down easily.

The sun is flaming over the Waitākere Ranges as I trot back down to the house, my step light and fast. Two bottles should be enough. For now, anyway – I'll probably run back up again later, or hop in a taxi to the 24-hour supermarket. Dinner, a bar somewhere, that's usually enough for the others – maybe an hour or two at Family if they're really up for it. They're not still awake at 4am, full of energy. Full of thirst, is the better word for it. My boyfriend, fast asleep in the bed next to me, he doesn't get it. He drinks and sleep takes him. For me, it's the opposite. Drink wakes me: wakes me up to all the things I need to do urgently. To smoke, and read, and write, and listen to music; to cry, and yearn hard for love, real love and understanding, for thrills, adventure, transcendence.

I open the little wooden gate to our house. The front door is open – laughter coming from out the back, Psychedelic Furs on the CD player. A soft summer twilight, the whole night in front of us. Someone hears the gate slam, shouts from the kitchen: 'Did you get the wine, babe? Hurry up, the tide's out!'

Just before I reach the doorstep I step to the left for a second. My bedroom is at the front of the house. I pull open the unlatched window, take one of the bottles out of the plastic bag, put it down quietly on the wooden floor inside, push the window closed again gently. 'Yes babe! I got it, don't panic, paramedics are coming!'

Years later Rebecca will tell me she always heard me lifting out the second bottle. A telltale clink of glass: 'I started to dread it.'

•

'I can't do this!' I'm sitting in front of my laptop, crying. The column was due an hour ago: guest posts from Fashion Week for a brand-new website. My laptop is damaged, the letter e isn't working. You could probably get a drink out of that keyboard by now, if you were desperate, I've spilt that much red wine on it.

'What's wrong?' My boyfriend comes over. His voice sounds tired, if I'd been in a state to notice.

'I'm trying to write but my keyboard is bro-ooo-ken.' I break into sobs. He slaps my thigh lightly, shoves me over. Sits in front of the computer, wrinkles his nose.

'Jesus, this thing is fucked – what have you been doing to it?'

We're in the little sunroom at the front of my bedroom, the place I go when he's asleep, the place I sit for hours, sipping away on a tiny glass. I won't use anything bigger; because it's a small glass, I'm not really drinking.

He brushes his hand over the keyboard, and a soft cloud of cigarette ash rises up like a phantom. 'Yeah, this is buggered,' he says flatly.

'I KNOW it is,' I scream at him. 'The e doesn't work! How the fuck can I write without e?'

He tries the e button, tapping down hard. I shove his hand off the keyboard.

'I told you, it doesn't work, leave it alone!'

He looks at me. I haven't been home before 4am the last three nights. But it's not like I was working, and it's not like I only stay out late when it's Fashion Week, either. Last week he texted me after work to ask me to bring home some green beans for dinner. When I put my key in the lock at 8am, he didn't even say anything, just stood there all fresh and clean from the shower, looking at me like someone he knew only vaguely.

'I'm sorry about your column,' he says quietly. 'I'm going to go to bed now, I've got work in the morning.'

Something stirs in my belly. He's not going to help me. 'Fine. I'll figure it out. You just go to bed then.' I pull the glass doors of the sun porch shut with a vengeance. Fuck him. I'll do it myself. And then afterwards, maybe I'll text the boys and meet them at Family. Half the time when I go out the front window in the middle of the night, he doesn't even notice.

Two nights later, we are lying in bed. 'Do you want to break up with me?' I say to the darkness.

There's a silence that makes me cold. I always ask this, he always says no, that's how it goes.

'Maybe.'

'What?'

A pause.

'Yeah, I want my life back.'

'Go then.' I say, without hesitation. The shame burns low in my belly.

All his stuff is gone by the weekend. Elliot moves in not long after.

●

When it happens, I'm in the middle of talking. My chest tightens, and all the words fall out of my head without warning. My thoughts are a pack of cards spread out all over the floor of the studio. I give a low gasp that no one hears and shut my eyes against the force of it. There are guests, thank God – one in Wellington, one in Dunedin maybe. The Wellington guy takes my sudden pause as an invitation. His voice drones on in my cans while I'm flicking the mic off, heaving forward on my elbows, filling up my lungs desperately. Where's all the air gone? My vision narrows, black margins moving closer together. I see myself from above suddenly, flailing at the desk, dying like a fish out of water. I must look like I'm having a heart attack, which is what this feels like. But there's no one to see it. The studio on the other side of the big pane of glass from me is empty. The whole show is coming out of Wellington today.

I keep breathing, trying to slow it down. Every part of my body is screaming: get out, get out, something's happening, you're dying. But I can't get out. There's not even a delay button.

The champion talker sounds like he's winding down, leaving longer and longer pauses for me to agree with him. 'Good point,' I wheeze, no idea what he's on about. The producer's in my ear, the next phone guest is waiting. Words. I need words. I blink once, twice, three times, until the screen in front of me swims into focus. I'm always surprised how many people think live radio is just turning up and talking. There's a script. There's always a script. Well, there is at National Radio. I squint and read the words on the screen, one after the other, leaning on them like a walking stick with my heart thumping. It's so loud, I'm sure the mic will pick it up – this whole show must sound like a sonogram. I grit the words out between small sips of air. One. After. Another. At some point I've said enough sentences for someone else to butt in and take over. I drink some water, spill the glass putting it down. Things continue, for an amount of time that is endless. No riffing. Short sentences. My fingers slip off the mouse several times, they're so sweaty. I'll die here if that computer goes dark for any reason. Towards the end of the hour, the adrenaline tapers and my teeth start chattering. I set my molars together, tasting the bile at the back of my throat, bitter and dirty. But the big clock opposite is ticking us closer. Thirty seconds before five, the theme soars up. My mic is off, the pips are starting. The producer down in Wellington says 'good show' like he always does. I sit back on the wheelie chair, cans still on, so it's like I'm underwater. I forgot to turn the lights on earlier, but even in the gloom I can see my fingers trembling. I lean forward, lower and lower until my forehead is touching the desk; clammy skin on thin upholstery. The same swirly, indistinct purply-green pattern that's been the same for the couple of years I've been here, having graduated from student radio. I breathe in the dusty, somehow *alive* smell of the studio. In spite of the panic attack, I feel safe here. My place. This is my place. Even though I am wrecking it.

•

Someone from a TV production company is on the phone. RNZ's my bread and butter, but I'm still a freelancer and this sounds lucrative. What morning can I do next week? I get my diary out, dark blue with 2008 in gold on the cover; flick through Monday – no, that's a dinner, and a launch on Tuesday, drinks after work on Wednesday, and Thursday nights are just generally a write-off. I turn five pages. There's no morning next week that I'm not going to be hungover. We get the meeting pencilled in for an afternoon instead. I hang up the phone and at the back of my head a bell has started ringing. 'Normal people don't drink like this,' a little voice says to me. 'It's not normal, not to be able to meet people on a weekday morning.' Just a small voice, low but insistent.

•

I'm sitting opposite a woman who is spooning up ramen carefully. A year ago, when things first started getting tense with my ex, this woman brought me to a community hall in an inner-city suburb. The room was big and draughty and wood panelled. On the low stage were a couple of plastic chairs. More chairs in rows either side of them. Banners hung down, numbered commandments, in black and red. They looked ominous. Searching and fearless, powerless, unmanageable, moral inventory: the language was arcane and frightening somehow. One by one, people mounted the stairs, sat on the chairs and addressed the group. They were visibly distressed, some of them. Talking about cravings, misery, self-obsession. One of them was self-harming, she said. I felt no connection to any of them. Afterwards, my friend asked me what I thought. I said, if you love drinking so much, or taking drugs or whatever, why couldn't you just get better at doing it? This is all about balance, surely? I never missed work, or a deadline for my column. Why couldn't they just cut down a bit? Go home early? My friend just smiled. 'Take what you want and leave the rest,' she said. I didn't want any of it.

We've stayed in touch, though I've never gone back to the community hall with her. But now, eating our ramen, the events of the last few weeks running through my mind – lying to our agent about why I need a new front door key, missing our rent, the thing with the taxi driver – I ask her: 'What will happen if I go back to the meetings, but I'm not really an addict or an alcoholic?'

She shrugs her narrow shoulders. 'I don't know. I guess you go for a while, and then stop because you don't need to be there? Not that big a deal, really.'

A pause. 'And what if I am an alcoholic, and I don't go? What will happen then?'

She moves her spoon to one side, picks up a pair of chopsticks delicately. 'It will get worse. Addiction is progressive.'

For the next twelve months, I replay those words over and over. Looking over all the excuses, the rationalisations, the plausible-but-untrue explanations for whatever sordid drama is playing out on the week in question. On April Fools' day I text a friend: I'm pregnant. She takes a long time to answer – and when she does, she is so sympathetic, but at the same time unsurprised, it stops being funny. But what I tell myself is: it's not getting worse. I still have my friends, my job, my house, my money. I go wherever I want, do whatever I want, answer to nobody. In quieter moments, I can admit, the thought of the future scares me. But at least I am holding it all together.

•

There's a particular way shock takes you when you're badly hungover – it's not just that you start shaking, the whole world does. I'm lying in bed, heart pounding, looking at the text from

Elliot. The events of last night flash by in disjointed pictures, only one or two clear images. One is of standing in front of an apartment door, the mirror of our own one, and knocking on it.

The enmity between the building manager and me has been there since the day we moved in. I watched her walking into our new place, looking around at all our stuff with her seagull eyes, and felt a distinct sense of invasion. I think she thinks we don't deserve the apartment, that we are too young and too dissolute to live somewhere so lovely. I agree with her, to be honest. We've landed in a penthouse, somehow: all very '90s with yellow walls and lots of glass-topped surfaces. From the balcony, you can see all the way over the bridge that spans the harbour. We got this place despite having no references and only a little money. But I am on the radio regularly now, and I have a newspaper column – maybe that swung it.

I am wearing a red lei in the photos and carrying a pair of black spectacles. I got them at a party – flashes of a DJ playing MGMT, and looking at a new pattern on the sleeve of my dress, little cigarette burns, light-coloured circles with a black border.

I think it was the lift that threw me: I'd never lived somewhere with different floors before. I get out on the wrong floor, and that is where the building manager finds me. Most likely some poor neighbour called her. All I remember is something flashing in my face suddenly, a light in my eyes, like a doctor would use, only brighter. I raise my hand up to bat it off, and get to my feet, the light still flashing. I turn to try my key again, turn back when someone calls me. That's the main photo they use in the Sunday paper, me all puffy-faced and vacant-eyed and garlanded, outside a door that says 5C. At least I'm standing up in this photo; there's another one of me, still asleep beside a bottle of blue Powerade, some pie crumbs and a packet of Watties frozen lasagne I bought at the dairy.

The photos went to the property manager, who sent them on to me, which was kind of her. I gave her some bluster about my privacy, then sent them to some people for a laugh, which is how they ended up in the paper. Since then, the building manager and I have been at loggerheads, and now I've gone and knocked on her door at 3am to have it out with her.

We leave without fuss. I don't want to be in the papers again, for one thing. I send an old friend an email: Do you think I should stop drinking? She'd laughed so hard at all of it, the powerade, the lasagne, I honestly thought she'd reassure me. 'I don't know, it's a very private thing,' she replies. I delete the email.

•

I do not know, at this point, how the people I work with are able to ignore the general air of chaos that surrounds me. The clothes from the night before, brand-new samples borrowed from designers' workrooms, slept-in, cigarette-burned, crumpled. The wild hair, the shaking hands – if nothing else, the smell of it. Wine stinks, the morning after. So does vodka. I've been in the papers again too, for being a plagiarist. I've been starting the Afternoons show with essays based on things I'm reading in English newspapers. Mornings pass in a blur of panic, exacerbated by crushing hangovers. I do not always attribute these articles. The journalist rings my phone one morning, leaves me a message. I listen to it in the bathroom of the man I have been drinking with the night before, bent over the sink, vomiting. The rawness after purging is depleting and exhausting. But it feels good to do it. Something about the ritual of running the tap until the water is really cold, making a fork of two fingers and pushing them down my gullet. Even if it's only a little bit of clear stuff that comes up, I feel better afterwards. I listen to her saying please get in touch, she'd love to talk to me, then I jab the buttons savagely, delete the message forever. I was banging out those intros five minutes before the hour, on three hours' sleep if I was lucky. Word theft. I think about my professor at college, steepling his fingers together, calling me radical.

The mirror's over the sink – I look up into it. My cheeks, two flames in a white mask, puffy and bloated. Lately, when I am drinking, I talk about Jesus. I can't remember this, I only know when it's repeated back to me the next morning. Everyone is sick of hearing about Christmas night, about how cold it must have been, the breath of the oxen on the baby Jesus. 'Imagine that,' I say, to people trying to get drunk in peace and quiet. 'Imagine the bitter cold of it!'

I stare at myself in the mirror, a bottle of aftershave in its midnight-blue glass bottle alongside me, hear Mammy's voice, silky with Carling, pointing at Baby Jesus in her crib on the marble. 'They looked after him, sure God love us, the cows and the donkeys.'

There's a morning, not long after that one. I'm walking down Hobson Street to the station – late again, and a drumbeat in my head, relentless. I look at the cars, flying up towards the motorway in great silver shoals, and I think how easy it would be to just step out and go under one, how comforting that idea feels, how obvious.

•

A big gin and tonic, somewhere between 2 and 3am. If I'd known it was going to be my last drink, I'd have put ice in it. I bring it over to the sofa, amid the remains of a dinner party. In the supermarket earlier I filled up the trolley with focaccia bread, mozzarella, out-of-season basil and tomatoes. Champagne even, and paid for all of it. I know Elliot is still mad about us having to leave the apartment. Now he's in bed, it's just me and my glass of Beefeater. These are my favourite drinks, the ones you don't need but have anyway.

The next morning, I wake early. Faint judder of cars going over the bridge, eleven storeys under me. The air's already full of the emptiness of Sunday. At the foot of the bed, the mirrored door of the wardrobe is slightly open. A couple of new dresses are hanging at the front, pristine and colourful. I imagine them covered in cigarette burns, hems ripped, dirty.

A man I was with came back to the apartment with me recently. The next morning, he said he watched as I leaned over the toilet, puked into it, leant back and shouted 'I'm so bored' before passing out on the floor. He said this in a subdued voice and asked me if I wanted to talk about it. I laughed and said it sounded like we should have stayed out longer. Secretly, I am frightened. Flash of Mammy, sitting at the pull-down table in the caravan in Kerry. Cheap wood veneer and scratchy upholstery. The carton of milk on the table, with the big red rose on it. Sipping her mug of tea, coppery spiral perm, face white with nausea. 'No postmortems, Noelle,' she'd say firmly. 'It's too early.'

I spend the day in bed, typing things into Google until the pillows get damp under me: 'How do you know if you're an alcoholic?' The various tenets and contradictions of Twelve Step philosophy. Cartesian dualism. You know you're in trouble when the solution looks worse than the problem. I rang a helpline a few weeks back. I'd woken up to a message from a guy I had no memory of meeting, saying he might have my handbag at his place in West Auckland. The woman who answered sounded too nice for me to be bothering her with my problems. She said there was a place in Kingsland, was I open to having an assessment?

I spent the next week deleting voicemails, wondering why in the fuck I gave her my real number.

It's the middle of winter. The light goes out of the day early. I make toast, watch *Buffy the Vampire Slayer*, fall asleep with the laptop humming on my chest like a cat, dream of a plane falling out of the sky in flames while I stand there watching.

The next day I text someone: I think I've stopped drinking.

She texts back: Go to a meeting.

Fifteen

On a low wall at the top of a steep street, I smoke a cigarette in the darkness. Across the road, there's a light in the doorway. Two men are leaning in it, also smoking. From the window on the first floor, a yellow glow is shining through the edges of the curtain. The people I need are in that room, the woman I texted told me.

I cross and uncross my legs, the wall is damp and cold beneath me. The cigarette tastes awful. It's been three days. They've passed slowly, mostly, although the hours between deciding to go to this place and finding myself outside it seem to have gone by in a heartbeat. It's not like I'm craving a drink, more that it is impossible that I will not have one. Maybe not tonight, maybe not tomorrow. But soon. Saturday is always a good day.

I inhale another clumsy lungful of tobacco, tearing my throat in the process. Realisation number one of the new era:

I'm terrible at smoking. I jeered at Mammy when she'd scrabble around looking for half-smoked butts in the early mornings. But I had the same contempt for her drinking, and where did that get me?

The men across the road scrape the ends of their cigarettes on the doorway, I watch the little orange sparks fly up and go out in the darkness. I squash a half-smoked Marlboro Light beneath one of the yellow high heels I got for 20 dollars in Paper Bag Princess, pull down the green skirt of my dress and push my bag higher on my shoulder. My jacket is buttoned up already. I try to pull it even closer. What am I doing, going in here? I nearly laugh. How can this possibly fix me?

And then I'm 9, or 10 maybe, sitting opposite Mammy in a small cold room that smells of blood and disinfectant.

'Get my nightdress.' Her voice, with all the life washed out of it. 'My white nightdress, get it out of the wardrobe. And Noelle' – low and urgent, she won't look at me saying it – 'get a packet of Stayfree as well for me. Over in the supermarket.'

Why is she telling me this, with Daddy standing there? My face is flaming. But she's insistent. 'You know where they are, which aisle? Make sure and get them.' Yes, yes. All right, I say, so she'll stop going on about it. Along one side of her head, there's a gauzy bandage, the hair around it is dark and clotted. She got out of a taxi and went over the wall in the front garden. Skull fracture, a small one.

The light's still bright across the way, the lit window and a glowing doorway. I can see shadows moving behind the curtain. My fingers are cold. I shove a hand in my pocket, worry at the inside of my jacket where the silk lining is ripped open. Once I copied an 0800 number out of the paper for her. 'Please go and get some help, please,' I wrote, in neat letters that I was still learning to join up properly.

She must have been to AA by then, already. 'Boring fuckers. Up on McCurtain Street, drinking tea and talking about one another.'

I think of the cans of Carling I poured the salt into. I'd laugh and laugh as she leant over the kitchen sink retching. 'You bad-minded bitch, what did you do to me?'

Please go and get some help, please.

The Smirnoff bottle with the blue label, next to the empty ice tray on the kitchen table in Hollymount. My bottle of Beefeater on the counter last Sunday.

For a second I'm so angry, so consumed by the irony, my lip curls up in a growl in the darkness. The cold air stings my front teeth and I shiver. My legs are cold through my thin black stockings. Up on the ridge, the green buses are purring past McDonald's. I think about texting someone, going back down the hill to SPQR for the second least expensive bottle. Nobody would even know that I tried to stop and couldn't. I look over at the door, still wide open. What if someone recognises me? The coat I'm wearing is the one in my byline for my newspaper column, bright plaid with brass buttons. What if they know me from the radio? I'm through the door across the road, and walking up the wooden stairs before I know it.

Inside, the room is very hot. There are long cloth banners in front of the window, not curtains. A mixture of ancient chairs line the walls and a low table is full of books and clear plastic biscuit barrels. The ceiling seems canted, lower than it should be. It's like being on a boat. I spread my feet, trying to get my balance. Everything here is shabby, and old-fashioned. I take a dark-blue book from a pile on the table. The fabric cover is threadbare and shiny from years of handling. My chair is a battered recliner; when I sit in it, my feet fly out to nearly eye level. I wish I hadn't worn this tartan jacket. It's too loud, the check is blaring. And the round brass buttons. I look like Sergeant Pepper, with my arse on the floor and my legs in the air. My face is red, I can feel it. I lie back, trying not to burst out crying.

There's a homeless man asleep in the chair opposite me, furry dreadlocks wrapped around his neck, lap full of chocolate chip cookies. I know him from the strip I think, from sitting outside SPQR. I took a taxi driver home with me a few months ago. I made him bring me to the Countdown in Grey Lynn for a box of Corona first and then brought him in to watch *Shortland Street*. I had a week of episodes taped on the Sky box. He went out and took the sign off the cab at 3am when I said he could stay over. He said his wife was dead, maybe? In Bulgaria. He was very hairy. I'm still dreaming about planes falling out of the sky. I asked a therapist about it. 'Sounds self-explanatory,' she said, not giving me much to work with.

She has coarse skin and a wide flat nose. Nice brown eyes. She writes me out receipts in an old-fashioned invoice book like I'm going to file them away carefully. After we finish every Wednesday, I walk down the narrow stairs in my yellow heels and I go into her dank little toilet and put on more lipstick. Lady Danger.

I'm rereading *Dracula*. Over and over, late at night, early morning, lying on my bed, smoking out the window in my yellow dress with the blue daisies and wine stains on it. Jonathan Harker uses a diary to try to keep his mind in order. I write things down, but I can't read my handwriting the next morning. There's a scrap in my make-up bag in shouting capitals: NO ONE IS GOING TO RESCUE YOU. No one rescued Jonathan Harker. He came down that wall himself, hanging on by his fingernails, nearly lost his mind doing it. But they do not go out alone, Mina and Van Helsing, Arthur, Quincy, Dr Seward and Jonathan Harker. The Crew of Light. They band together, bare their shameful secrets (those sexy vampire ladies in the castle, Jonathan!). It is only by helping and receiving help in return from one another that they are able to defeat the monster. The thing that wants to eat them up, destroy them. Everyone in this strange little meeting room is on my team now. Including the sleeping dreads guy, if he wants to be. And the woman sitting opposite, with the hiking boots, who brought her own muesli.

•

Newly sober, and raw as a rubbed eyelid, my God is in the Sky Tower. I come home at midnight, 1, 2, 3 o'clock in the morning, rattling from a night in front of a lemonade pretending there's vodka in it, and open the ranch slider on the mean little balcony of my apartment on Pitt Street. I sit on the ridge between the slider and the tiles in the cold August air and smoke Marlboro Lights that I hate the taste of and look out over the city to where the hypodermic rises into the sky a block and a half away, and I ask someone, anyone to look after me. I don't know if they will, or if they won't, but the asking becomes something of a ritual, comforting in itself at the end of another long day of uncertainty.

Everything I do now tires me – an exhaustion that gets so deep into your bones, you can't get out of the shower, and when you do, you just stand there for ages, shivering and dazed with a towel around you. I go to work at the radio station every day without a hangover, hating it. At least I wasn't bored when I was dealing to the shakes every morning, jamming my elbow into the gap between my hard drive and the computer monitor to brace my hand enough to hold a pot of yoghurt. Repairing to the disabled toilet afterwards to vomit it up discreetly, pushing my fingers far enough down the back of my throat to get the bile up, swiping my streaming eyes in the mirror, cleaning my teeth with my index finger.

But I go to work, just like everyone else does, take myself down Vincent Street in the cold every morning. I make soup, from a Jamie Oliver recipe, that requires an awful lot of celery. I put the whole pot of it in the fridge because I don't have any plastic containers. I stop answering texts that I used to. Some of them anyway. I still go out constantly. I drink a lot of V and try not to hear the sound of my own stupid voice banging in my temples. People might think that when you stop drinking, things get better. They don't. They get worse to begin with. Of course they do. I am bare, flayed, missing a layer.

One morning, about a month into it, I lie in bed rigid. I have a writing deadline and I'm due at the radio station, but I am frozen to the mattress. All the anxiety of the last however many years has risen up inside me. I visualise the kettle in the kitchen, imagine getting up and turning it on. If I could just make a cup of tea, maybe I could start the day. But I can't move, I'm too frightened. Pure, wild fear, galloping inside me. I am mad. That's what I am most afraid of. That I've stopped drinking, only to reveal a deeper pathology. I lie on the bed under the flowery duvet, and see years running away from me. I'll be here forever. I am 30 years old, with no money, no home except a sterile rental, a flatmate who doesn't talk to me much anymore. I get up eventually and boil the kettle; I am too afraid not to.

'I wouldn't wish early recovery on my worst enemy,' my sponsor tells me. She says things like 'You need to stop running on your own will, and hand it over'. Or: 'Whatever you're holding onto the hardest, that's what you need to hand over.' Every time she talks about handing it over, I imagine myself as Mary in a Nativity Play, holding a swaddled bundle. Where am I supposed to put my bundle, exactly? And what is in it? What the fuck is she talking about? I just want to stop drinking, I don't remember signing up for a crackpot course in symbolism.

I tell nobody I've stopped. Nobody notices. There's a club just off High Street we all go to. One night I order two vodka tonics and line them up on the table in front of me. I eyeball the tall frosted glasses, anticipating a quietness inside my head, a bit of fucking comfort. My upper back is covered in painful red spots. A naturopath in Kingsland takes one look at it and says I am 'hardcore detoxing'. I give the vodka tonics away, walk up Queen Street with a fresh packet of Marlboro Lights, thinking of the maudlin Cat Power song I'd been listening to on repeat.

The Sky Tower is pink when I get home. For breast cancer. I sit and look out at it, the largest antenna in the country. I imagine jagged waves radiating out from it, like those cartoon radio towers in 1930s newsreel broadcasts. The tallest tower in the Southern Hemisphere – surprising there's nothing in Sydney taller. I watch it pierce a big scudding black cloud and I will myself to believe in something bigger than me. Something that wants me to be safe and happy. I am sick of feeling dirty.

Over the course of a few of these sorts of nights, I find myself looking forward to coming home to the Sky Tower. It's easy to leave the club, not look twice at the fat-bellied little shot glasses of tequila that are slid over the bar along with my lime and soda. I watch the lights across the CBD from my eyrie on Pitt Street, behind the low-rent Korean karaoke dive, looking out over the lovely art deco Fire Station, down the curve of Hobson Street and back up the Hill to the big needle. Inside, it'll be full of hopefuls feeding pokies, no clocks on the walls anywhere in the casino. I can imagine them all, and I feel sad for them suddenly. It is the first time I've thought about anyone but myself, my own mess of a life, in ages. I smoke, watch the twinkling vista, all the lights out there in central Auckland, all connected to me, maybe, in ways I can't fathom, but that someone is in charge of. Someone not me, bigger than me. This is praying. It takes hold and life gets a bit easier. I start sleeping. I keep not drinking. A friend takes me to buy a mattress and a base from a budget place in Mt Wellington, the first new bed I've ever slept in. Showers get easier to get in and out of. I start to feel cleaner. I keep not answering certain texts and emails. I buy an iPod in a pink leather case and listen to You Just Haven't Earned it Yet, Baby while walking over Hopetoun bridge to AA meetings.

Alexander McQueen is found dead in his wardrobe a few months after I stop drinking. I print out images from his runway shows, headpieces made of birds of prey and clouds of butterflies, beautiful women in couture straitjackets, screaming. Sitting watching the Sky Tower, I start to feel my outlines. A woman in a city, relatively blameless for the first time in ages. There is less and less to be afraid of.

I get a bus that picks me up at the corner of Richmond Road and Ponsonby Road, where Golden Dawn was. It takes me to the community centre in time for the lunch meeting. I walk down the hall, past the Citizens Advice Bureau and the Plunket office, in my red rubber Vivienne Westwood platforms that smell like lollies, keeping my head down. I'm not ashamed, but I don't particularly want to bump into any new mothers. I sit by the door in a blue plastic chair that says 'Property of Auckland Council', half close my eyes, smell the familiar smell of sun-warmed dust and old carpet tiles. High up on the wall directly beneath the ceiling is a long mural depicting the shops up on Surrey Crescent. It's done in a cartoony, fake-graffiti style that's aged badly.

Across from me, the smallest girl in a group of girls is sobbing quietly as the others crowd around her. Treatment centre girls.

They're all wearing jandals and tracksuits that look like pyjamas. There's a lot of crying in treatment. I wouldn't know. I was too busy for rehab. Too scared for it, more likely. From time to time, I still find the reality of my new existence overwhelming. Last month, I went to a recovery camp-out: a whole weekend avoiding games of volleyball and retching at the coleslaw at dinner. At some point it hit me, this was it for me from now on, recreationally speaking, and I spent the rest of the time there on a top bunk under a scratchy blanket, crying.

After the meeting I get some food in the uptight wholefoods shop on the corner where my friend got asked to leave once, when she went in with a vintage fur coat on. I buy a pie, lentils in a brick of pastry, and sit at the bus stop. There's nothing to do except be in the afternoon. I feel lighter, in the way I always do after a meeting. I don't know how it works, but there's an ease after being there.

The bus comes and I hop on. We ride along the curve of the road, past the roundabout on Peel Street, opposite the big stone villa on the corner. The bus picks up speed on the downhill, banana trees and the big green Countdown flying past the window, and I am filled suddenly with a fierce, clean joy that comes out of nowhere. I will be 31 in a few months and that terror I used to feel of life, that black and leaping fear of growing up and buying whiteware – I don't have it anymore. I don't know when it left me. The bus rolls along Richmond Road, back up towards Ponsonby and I know without needing to look that there's a glint of blue water behind us. At this angle on the road, a trick of perspective means the sea is in the sky in front of you. The bushes that line the road are full of passionfruit vines and spiky, colourful bird-of-paradise flowers. I watch the kids in their school uniforms chugging Cokes, women at the bus stop, just normal workers going about their business, and I don't hate them the way I used to. I am just a person among people, no better and no worse. I am nearly six months sober.

I go home to Ireland a few months later. I do not tell Mammy or Daddy that I am in recovery directly. I hear Mammy on the phone one night saying 'Noelle doesn't drink at all, anymore' to someone, in the same tone of voice she once used to say I had a photographic memory, or God bless us, she's very photogenic. She buys a white hydrangea called Noelle, she tells us. The plant sits in a pot in my bedroom until I go back to New Zealand, after which she plants it and sends me photos of herself pointing at it as it slowly covers the back garden. 'Look, look, Noelle is getting bigger.' Noelle creeps across the back garden, flowering white first, and later blue and purple. Mammy buys a stone elephant with an upraised trunk and a fat Buddha to put beneath her.

Sixteen

SMALL ADULT is printed on the inside of the blood pressure cuff – it's twice the width of the arm she holds out obediently. The nurse is blonde, as they all seem to be, nice girls from up the country. They are all called Aoife, Ciara and Roisin. I wonder if they are as surprised as I am that it is Saturday now, and Mammy is not dead yet. She was playing with her morphine pump when I came in, but she still seems quite compos mentis, apart from wanting to ring her father.

'They're all afraid of it,' she looks at me, eyes burning.

'Afraid of what?'

'Ah the thing, the thing they're all getting, they're afraid of it, don't be so stupid.'

She must mean Covid. They said in the paper this morning that numbers are climbing in Italy. There's a security guard out front now, with a list you have to be on for visits, and a big clear globe of hand sanitiser you have to use before going into the main building. I hate the chemical smell it leaves on my fingers, the unnatural way it dries instantly.

I burrow down in my chair, soft scratch of my red wool coat against my wrists and elbows. I'm still in the extended surprise that, even though she is taking her time with it, my mother is actually dying. I can't post any of the photos I take of her to Instagram, they're too frightening.

·

'Sure she's her mother now, the very image of her.' My godmother is wearing a purple sleeveless puffa jacket that makes her look like a schoolgirl. I'm showing her the photos of Mammy, wild eyed, big nosed, skeletal. I've seen similar photos of Han before she died, the flesh gone from her bones, sitting in her chair by the fire in Chapel Hill, smoking.

She is sitting across from me, eating a wrap with chicken and lots of sauces. I'm having the salty, indeterminate soup they are legally required to serve everywhere in Ireland at lunchtime. We fell into this pub, out of yet another rainstorm. Gusts of cold hit my back every time the door opens.

'She was very good. She was very good when ye were small, I mean. I know there was neglect in other ways, over the alcohol.' She says it fast, takes a tidy bite, gestures to the air with a neat little hand. Swallows. 'But I always remember, she had the four of ye – and I was just living a few doors down that time. She'd be walking the road, day in, day out, showing ye every single bird, every single tree and bush, and I don't know what. She did!' Her eyes are round at the memory. There's a good-size emerald on her left hand. She looks the same as she looked as a bridesmaid, standing with my mother at the altar over forty years ago; small and fair and pretty. 'Every bird, every tree, she knew them all. And she told ye all the names of them. Never stopped talking to ye, she didn't. I used to look at her, and I'd think, Jesus I'd never have the patience to do it, with my two.'

After lunch, I wander aimlessly. It's weirdly luxurious, this freedom from responsibility, the sands of paid childcare no longer running down on me, the salty taste of soup in the back of my throat, the bleachy-fleshy antiseptic smell of the hospital still stuck in my nostrils. I remember the walks, the ones my godmother was talking about; out the road up to Clogheen, following the spine of the cracked stone walls to the top of the boreen by the old-fashioned water pump, me and my brother running on ahead, Mammy pushing Sarah in the buggy. Picking blackberries, finding ladybirds, the breathless stillness when one would perch on my knuckle, the neat perfection of her black spots on the red body, a big outbreath as she whirred into life, the spotty dome parting down the middle, gauzy wings unfolding tiny and ingenious. Rising up, letting the air take her. *Ladybird, ladybird, fly away home.* Did Mammy really teach us all the names of things? In my memory, I knew them already. We went to university, all four of us. No one in Mammy or Daddy's family ever did third level. Daddy left school at 12, as Mammy never ceases to tell us.

She was asleep when I left her, curled up small on the narrow bed, a puff of pink bed socks at one end and a little blob of woolly hat at the other. I found the beanie last week in my favourite flower shop down in Douglas Street, the same one I email from New Zealand for her deliveries, every birthday, anniversary and Christmas. 'A big bright bunch, no lilies.' There was a basket of hats – made by a local 16-year-old, the sign said, to raise money for Peru or somewhere like that. Her grandmother helps her knit them, the owner, an open-faced girl in overalls, told me. I bought one, reeling from the wholesomeness. Pink and white, Mammy's colours. She didn't say much when I brought it over, but she was pleased enough when we came back the next morning. 'The nurse told me I look like an ice-cream cone.' Gesturing to the hat, the bed socks, the velour blanket. 'They think I'm cracked in here, sure.' Rolling her eyes, loving it. She rarely took it off after that. I was glad I bought it. I'd wavered at the time, afraid she'd scorn it, that it was a waste of money.

Back to the pub we had lunch in earlier. It's dark and welcoming at this time of the evening, the warm, bready smell of beer and stout in the air mixed with the coal fire. Ten years without a drink, there are still moments when I miss it. John Paul goes to the bar with his backpack still on – as far as I know he's been living out of it. Robert is wearing his too, he's come from teaching. They look so young with school bags, both of them. Sarah puts her handbag down, opens it, briskly asking who needs drinks. I gesture at my tea in front of me; Robert asks for a low-alcohol Heineken, he has school again tomorrow. She goes to the bar and John Paul passes her on his way back down to us. He settles in the chair closest to the fire, puts his pint in front of him, sighs and sips the head of it. His fingers pull the hair in front of his forehead, the way they do when he is thinking, pulling the curls forward into a little pompadour over his glasses. I have seen him only infrequently since I got here, coffee in a hotel with him and his wife Juliet before a hospital visit, and once in the early morning at my sister's, before Juliet came over from England. I was up early, saying good night to Eve when he appeared at the door, pausing to put on his backpack. He'd come in late, spent the night on the sofa. He left to get a bus back up to Hollymount, didn't want coffee, or breakfast or a shower.

Juliet is gone back to London now, I'm not sure where he is sleeping. He visits the hospital at different times from me and my sister. I think he spends the rest of the evenings with my uncles, in some of the better pubs in the city.

'How's Eve?' he says, pushing back in his chair, and 'Very good, very good', when I say she's fantastic. He whispers 'fintistic' under his breath softly, mocking my New Zealand accent. The hand that twirls the hair doesn't stay still for a minute. I keep expecting him to stick his thumb in his mouth like he used to.

'He's your favourite, just admit it.' I've said this to Mammy more times than I can remember. He is the one, at least, whose company she craves. Born premature – 'his poor lungs were small, they took him to the neonatal, will I ever forget it?' – he's the only one she went overseas for. Years of visits while he was at Oxford, and then dropping everything every time he came home on his holidays.

'You're wronging me,' she would insist. 'May God forgive you, you're wronging me Noelle, I love you all equally.' But a blind man could see the delight they took in each other's company, the private bubble that surrounded them, their secret little sorties into The Mutton Lane whenever he was in Cork, their jokes, their characters, their stories. He calls her Momma, she calls him Forrest. He goes to the Mercy later in the evenings, when she's falling asleep, stands at the foot of her bed quietly. Several times he's said he's here 'for the duration'. Like it's a prison sentence. He's a barrister now, in London. He can take as much time off as he likes, apparently, even though he's only recently qualified.

The owner of the bar comes over to throw some coal on the fire, offers to get more milk for the pot of tea he made me earlier. He leans against the fireplace, with his gold signet ring and his open shirt and his expensive roundy glasses saying isn't the cold desperate, and haven't we the best seat in the house etcetera. John Paul and I exchange looks, I can see the word 'asshole' is coming out of his head in a speech bubble. Your man is a scion of Cork's hospitality sector, up to his neck in the Jazz Festival, the Rory Gallagher Museum probably, all that self-mythologising commerce that keeps this little city powered. He goes off to get my milk and John Paul and I have a pleasant moment, mocking him telepathically.

Sarah's texting now, sitting next to Robert, tapping away with one finger on the screen in a purposeful manner, French-tipped nails gleaming in the glow from the fire, glass of white wine in front of her. Her face in the blue light is tired. 'I'm meeting the girls later,' she says, putting the phone down. 'I'm having a night off tonight, someone else can ring the hospital.'

'Good for you,' I say, guiltily. Without her, Mammy's swift degeneration would have been even more chaotic. Sarah is the one who drove after the ambulance when they came up to shift her down to the Mercy. Mammy made them wait outside while she had her last cigarette in the utility room toilet. It was Sarah who got her settled in the hospital, who went into town and bought all the pink bedding. Sarah is the one Byrne looks at when I ask him questions, he probably knows better than I do that it's Sarah who is running this, who rings Mammy every day from work 'just checking in', who comes up to the house on Mother's Day with a box of Nestlé Dairy Box and a card with 50 Euro. She lives down the road from them now, has always been in the vicinity.

'Mammy and Daddy are great too, Noelle, and Cork is great, there's nothing wrong with it!' I remember her shouting at me, when she came out to New Zealand. I'd spent two weeks introducing her to all of my friends, many of whom were older than me, in couples. I didn't see it then, obvious parent substitutes. We sat at a picnic table, drinking vodka beneath the majestic mountain peaks in Queenstown, and she berated me for not seeing any value in our own parents. When Mammy dies, Sarah will lose a good friend, however surreal that seems to me. She flicks her long dark hair back, drinks her wine, looking over the rim of her glass at the three of us, alert as ever to all of the unspoken currents.

We left her out, me and John Paul, we used to. We were close in age, similar in our inclinations, holing up in the guest-room bed to make up fake news headlines and goggle over shark attack photos. Sarah was that bit younger, more sensitive, although then we called it stupid. More innocent, certainly. Her idea of a good time was singing all the songs from *The Little Mermaid*, one after another. I made her pay once, to go to the cinema together – pay extra like, on top of the ticket. *Titanic*, we went to. I even made her get the Freddos. She's in corporate accounts now, for a big multinational, making plenty of money, so the joke's on the rest of us. She gets up to get another round for everyone. 'Pint please, Annie,' John Paul says, gesturing. He calls her Annie after Kathy Bates's character in *Misery*. She calls him Roy after the guy in *Coronation Street* who wears his house key on a piece of string and has several times been in trouble for stalking women. I ask for a fizzy water. She goes off dutifully. She likes it when we are all together. She enjoys being indispensable. I've been using her Netflix account for the last four years – she pays extra to fit everyone.

I turn back to the fire and the pub, alive in the darkness. I like that it's just us, no husbands or wives, girlfriends, boyfriends, children. My pizza comes and Robert looks it over with professional interest. He spends a lot of time on TripAdvisor, comparing the lasagnes in local restaurants.

'He's there at the end of the bed when I wake up every evening, just standing there like a fucking undertaker,' Mammy told Sarah yesterday. As the youngest, he spent more time with them alone than the rest of us. They went on holidays together, hotels and five-star resorts in Kerry – even Portugal once, riding the back of the Celtic Tiger. He's lived at home for longer than anyone.

'Don't talk to me girl, I'm exhausted. I had a tutorial again last night,' Mammy would say on the phone to me. A tutorial is when Robert comes home from a night in town, and gets into the bed beside her, to talk about literature and poetry. 'Does he actually recite them?' I asked her. 'Go 'way girl, those two fucking roads in the wood, I'm demented from them. Two roads he's on about, smoking every fag in the house. I've none for the morning.'

Recently she said, he had her up at 3am explaining the concept of jeopardy. 'You have to have it, he says, in order for the narrative to be successful. You have to have jeopardy! Shut up I said to him,' and she sounded so happy telling me. 'Shut up about jeopardy, you've the whole house awake, can't you ever come home and just go to bed like a normal person?' I didn't ask her where she thinks he got it from.

Robert's face is very pale in the light of the fire as he pulls on his Heineken bottle. He said to me once, Mammy told him he was the cleverest and the most perceptive, but I think at 3am, to get him out of her bed, and away from her cigarettes, she would have said anything. 'She's dying, I know she's dying!' was the first thing he said to me when I arrived last week, almost shouting, as though I'd tried to convince him otherwise.

'The thing none of ye know about Mammy,' he said to me once, 'is that she's funny.'

We break apart naturally, after the second drink. Sarah goes first, flat-footed in her thin shoes, out past the smoking area. I know she will ring the ward later even if she says she won't.

I want to run out and put my arms around her. The boys walk out the door, knapsacks high on their backs, like a pair of Mormon missionaries. Then I head towards Sarah's house, to ring Eve and John. I walk fast in the cold, the moon flying along in the dark-blue sky above me, down dark narrow lanes that reek of moss and piss. I feel no fear. I grew up here.

Seventeen

On the crest of Hopetoun Bridge, I stop and take a selfie. I stretch my arm out straight so I get as much of me as possible into the photo. My hair is cropped short, and I'm wearing a big pair of lime green sunglasses. I've started getting fake tans, standing naked in a pop-up tent out the back of a beauty salon in Grey Lynn while an obliging older woman comes at me with a spray gun. You can see the thin, plum-coloured straps of the playsuit I'm wearing pop against my brown shoulders. My hair is ruffled by the light breeze blowing in off the water and I'm smiling, a bright wide grin that says hello and pleased to meet you. It's just before 7 o'clock on a Saturday evening, mid-January, the height of summer. Under the bridge, the motorways thrum and flash. From where I'm standing, you can see the harbour sparkling blue and white all the way to Rangitoto. I'm taking a selfie to fix myself here, in this place, in this moment. I'm on my way to meet someone. I'm nervous.

People do this, I tell myself. They do it all the time – go on blind dates, meet on dating apps, whatever. A friend put me in touch with the man I'm going to see, she thinks we'll enjoy each other. But the texting to set things up, suggesting a venue, it's all been a bit exposing already. Drinks and dinner, is all. But it isn't really. It's admitting I want this: a partner, a home, a family eventually. I used to look down on people who dared to work towards this stuff. I laughed at everyone who wasn't unironic about all the things that adult life requires: showing up for someone else, being faithful, paying taxes. I wouldn't dream of flirting, even, unless I had a drink in me. It's been a long time since I flirted with anyone. What's the line from *Friends* again? 'I haven't had sex in so long, I'm wondering if they've changed it.' Monica was always my favourite.

At the meeting earlier, I said that I was grateful. For all the things I have, and for the ability to participate in life the way I used to not be able to. I was thinking about tonight, coming out to meet this man I don't know, sitting in a restaurant, as naked and hopeful as any of the rest of them. I'm just a person in the world, no worse and no better. And that's OK – I say it out loud, and the wind takes it. That's OK, I say again. It's OK to go and meet this man, with my head screwed on and my heart open. A little bit open anyway. If he's an asshole, I can leave early. And I'm wearing flat shoes, I'll walk home if I have to. But what if I like him, and he doesn't like me back? What if it goes somewhere for a few weeks, and then he stops texting? What if he has a secret family, or he's a closet alcoholic? Please not that, I'll do anything but I can't go to Al-Anon again, sitting round the big table with all those poor women, that was terrible.

If he doesn't show, I'll have a Forget-Me-Not and talk to Dee – she's the one who set us up anyway, she vouched for him. I have friends here. I can do this. I stand on the bridge, harbour on one side, high-rises on the other. This is the city where I got sober, four-and-a-half years now. I've been away and back again – I just spent fifteen months back in Ireland, trying to be a writer. There's a manuscript in my desk drawer. I know it's not very good, but I'm glad I did it. I missed this city though. I dreamed of it – the melancholy light when the sun hits the trees in Western Park in April, turning the corner down to Ponsonby Road from the petrol station, the long swing of the ridge in front of me.

Crossing Beresford Square, I get a text. I stop to read it outside Supper Club, smiling involuntarily. 'I'm the bloke in the blue shirt by the bar,' it says. I've never had dinner with someone who calls himself a bloke before. A blind date. He could be anyone. But it's all right to want things. This is my city. And he's there already. I walk faster so as not to keep him waiting.

●

She comes into the bedroom before the sun's even up properly. 'Good morning! It is I, your mother!' It's from *Dirty Rotten Scoundrels*, when Michael Caine says 'It is I, your brother!' Mammy and John Paul are obsessed with that film, they act out long scenes from it: Dr Emil Schaffhausen, Ruprecht the Monkey Boy. 'Ruprecht, don't take the cork off the fork.' 'Why is the cork on the fork?' 'To prevent him hurting himself – and others.' Falling about laughing, the two of them.

She comes in, on her little creeping feet, and I groan like I'm dying.

'Why? Why are you so early? Why do you come in here and wake me?'

'Go 'way out of that, and you inside my bed that I made for you!'

'It's *my* bed!' But it's her room now, my old sage green one, full of Holy Pictures, and Lancôme box sets and leaflets for novenas.

The sheets are clean and sweet from the washing line, the same ones I grew up with, thin and soft as skin with faded patterns of pale flowers.

'Sit up, til I show you, I got you something.' Her eyes are shining.

'No more charity shop stuff Ma, I'm going back on Ryanair, I'm not paying for it!' I'm flying into Carcassonne, home to John's place. I am meant to be revising the novel I've spent a couple of years writing, a story about a girl who got her hand maimed when she tried to kiss a vampire. In my clearer moments I can see that it is objectively terrible – derivative, and embarrassing – and anyway, I can't work on it anymore, I'm too happy. Mammy is extremely interested in John, but limits herself to looking at the photos I show her on my phone and saying 'Are you sure he's tall enough? Ye must be hilarious the two of ye!'

'Do you want it or not?' She's standing at the end of the bed in her house clothes, grey tracksuit bottoms and a soft brown zip-up cardigan with flecks in the wool that make her eyes greener. She's started dying her hair bright pink, she gets the candy-coloured sachets from a Polish grocer's. One of the girls from the B&B where she cleans put her onto it. Weirdly, it suits her: her pale skin is warmed up by the colour, it makes her eyes sparkle and her cheeks look rosy. She likes working at the B&B, I think, although she gives out about it – 'Dragging that hoover up all them stairs, my back is broken.' It's a cavernous Victorian red-brick mansion owned by one of my father's friends, another plumber. The bathroom at Hollymount is full of miniature shampoos and gels left behind by tourists and groups of choral singers.

'Sit up and look, let you!' She puts her hands behind her back, like she did when I was small and I had to guess which hand held the present. 'Close your eyes and pick one. Come on!

No cheating!' I sit up, reach over, and slap her on the left shoulder. 'Ow, Noelle! You're so rough, my bones are frail.'

'Shut up, old woman – hand over my present.' She puts a little red paper bag in my hands, stuffed with pink tissue paper. I put my hand in, take out a tin of Vaseline, a lip gloss and a mirror.

'For the plane, to do yourself up before you see your fella.'

'Shut up. He's my boyfriend, not my fella. And that better not be second hand!' I turn the lip gloss up to check the colour.

'It is red. I know you. God you're so ungrateful' She puffs theatrically. 'Look, there's more in it.' I put my hand in the bag again, pull out a book. A man with a pipe, wearing a deerstalker. *The Collected Sherlock Holmes*, a free-with-a-magazine edition. 'Your favourite,' she says, proudly.

'No. *Dracula* is my favourite,' I correct her.

'Fuck off so –'

'But this is also good. I love him too. Where did you get this, out of interest?'

'Never mind where I got it.' One of her charity shops, the house is groaning with stuff. 'No matter what I do, ye're never grateful for anything. Go on back to France so, to your Monsieur, your new fella. You think you're great now, don't you?'

She's happy though, I can tell. Happy with the presents she has chosen. She shuffles off downstairs for a fag. Outside my bedroom window the trees that were puny when I was small are a long green canopy.

'Mammy!' I call her back at the door. When she turns around, I suck my cheeks in and push my lips out. 'Kissy kissy like the fishy.'

She does it too, purses her mouth up. 'Kissy kissy,' she says, and starts laughing. She shakes a finger at me, like Dr Schaffhausen. 'Noelle is very silly!'

I lie back on the pillow, her stuffed animals lying around me. I have an awful feeling the lip gloss is from the charity shop. I push it down the side of the bed. The book has someone's name written on the inside cover. I put it on the bedside table. The room is flooded with the soft light of morning.

•

'Leave him here sure, go on away you, if you want to!' Mammy is waspish, sick of me already.

I stare at her pinched little face, I want to slap it. Her skinny long fingers grasp the blonde pint on the table. I don't know what she's even doing here, she says she hates it. The night's ramping up behind us, they're two or three deep at the bar already. The DJ is setting up his mobile disco unit down by the Ladies.

Daddy wanders up, cheeks red from drink, looks with consternation at me and Mammy glaring at each other. 'What's wrong, Moll?'

'Nothing's wrong, I'm just saying I'm going.'

'Sure go on away so, we'll look after him for you' – jerking his head to where John is at the bar, deep in conversation with one of my uncles. I can tell by his agreeable, bemused expression that he's probably understanding one in every ten words that's said to him. He's six pints in – I know because I've had six Ballygowan sparkling waters. My throat is sore from the cold, there's too much ice in the glasses they keep putting in front of me. No matter where I look, I can see someone I'm related to, by blood or by marriage. I've been here for two hours now, and I've had enough of it. But everyone else is just getting started. My parents are staring at me, one with hostility and one in confusion. They don't understand, they never understand. I'm 12 again, shaking with fury.

'Listen,' I say, taking a breath, keeping my voice steady. 'This is lovely, it's great everyone came, Daddy' – the bar is full of my cousins – 'but we're getting a bus to Dublin first thing in the morning. And then after that, it's 32 hours back to Auckland. I'm tired now, and if he gets sideways tonight he'll be no use tomorrow.'

'Ah shut up, Noelle, sure he's grand. He's only here for the night – let him alone, would you?'

Fucking Mammy. She's always the same, she never wants to go home from anywhere, not even this place, that she hasn't darkened the door of for ages. This is Daddy's territory, full of his sisters and brothers. She used to ring up looking for him, until the barmaid started putting the phone back down on her. She's seething with resentment at everyone in here, but she'll still be the last to leave tonight, when everyone else is long gone home with a chicken supper.

I look away from the two of them, before I yell in their faces. My cousins are lined up on the banquette opposite, bottles of white wine in metal coolers in front of them. Three out of five Heaphy sisters, the ones I played with when we were children. My favourite one, Audrey, looked like Whitney Houston in the I Wanna Dance with Somebody video. They're all grown up now, with their big hair and Kardashian make-up. They are beautiful and tall and solid, and know exactly who they are and what they are doing. They have been coming down here to The Joshua Tree for Friday nights and 21sts and all kinds of celebrations for as long as I have been in New Zealand. They had a night for me before I left, the DJ played Boom, Boom, Boom, Boom (I Want You in my Room) and dedicated it 'to Noelle who is going to Australia'. I tried to explain it was Auckland, but no one could hear me over the music.

My Dad had his 60th here in the Josh two years ago. They all came and toasted him, my cousins and his sisters and brothers, all clapping and cheering when he whirled Mammy around the floor to the Country and Western the mobile DJ played especially. Mammy was in bed for three days after, said he fractured a rib, grabbing her. I came home to surprise him. There's photos of me and Mammy in sparkly cowboy hats, the DJ in the background. It's the last time we had a full family photo – even my brother came from Oxford for the night, to drink pints and eat cocktail sausages.

I'm so tired suddenly, I can't face another conversation about the weather, radio, the price of everything in New Zealand. Spoilsport, killjoy, me and my no drinking. The disco lights start flashing on the back wall, little globes of red and green and purple. The DJ plays a Kylie song, so loud it shakes the glasses on the table. 'Turn it down, would you? Do you think you're in Páirc Uí Chaoimh or what?' shouts Audrey, holding her ears dramatically. The DJ complies briskly. You wouldn't cross her. I find John at the bar, tell him I'll be back to pick him up in an hour.

'OK love, all OK? Whatever you like.' His eyes crinkle up at the sides when he smiles, they're slightly unfocused. His bottom shirt button is open, three fresh black-and-cream pints lined up in front of him.

'I like him,' Robert says, appearing beside me. He has a navy blue shirt on him that makes his eyes look brighter than usual, and that freshly washed-and-shaved air of purpose that marks all the young men in Cork when there's a long night in front of them. He smells of Jean Paul Gaultier and there's a full packet of cigarettes in his top pocket. 'He's a good stick, like. And he knows Kerouac. Good fella.'

'You're such a cliché, Robert', but I'm laughing. It's easy to like him the best when he's being nice to me.

'You know it, Noelle! "The only people for me are the mad ones, the ones who are mad to live, mad to talk, mad to be saved . . ."'

'Yeah, yeah, blah blah blah, First Arts Beatnik 101 – go and show John your BA, Robert.'

'I will too, and we'll have a drink on it. Because that's what we do, it's Friday night baby and you can't any more, hahaha, Noelle. Old woman. I bet you miss it! "Burn, burn, burn, like fabulous yellow roman candles . . ."'

I push him off and he goes, laughing. What I wouldn't give right now for the clean chemical burn of a double shot of vodka, tasting it sharp and cold as a sword going through me. For a second, I'm seized with the need to say fuck it, elbow my way back to the bar, start calling drinks and see where it takes me.

They turn up at the hotel, Mammy and Daddy, at 5.45 the next morning – Mammy with a pile of John's washing she's got her hands on somehow. They make us go to the dining room, even though I say I only drink coffee at this time of the morning. Inside, they fill their plates from the buffet. Full Irishes, the watery scambled eggs making me nauseous. Mammy makes a small pile of butter pats, wraps them in a napkin. 'Very handy to have, they are,' she says, as she's done for the last twenty years in every restaurant. John, slightly green, picks at some rashers and toast delicately.

'How many pints do you think your Dad had last night?' he whispers, nodding over to where Daddy is stacking hash browns on a lake of baked beans and grinning over at me. 'Grand breakfast all the same, Moll, we'll be back here won't we?'

'Ten, he told me.' John shakes his head in disbelief.

'How many did you have?' I'm curious, and despite myself, proud of my father.

'Oh about eight, I reckon. And that was giving it a nudge.' He sips his coffee gingerly. 'They're machines. I haven't drunk like that since university.'

He says Daddy took him out to the smoking lounge and told him to take care of me, and then Robert kept him out there for another hour, talking about Wilfred Owen. I'm laughing as he sits beside me, this man who can stand at the bar with my Dad and my brother and my uncles, with his deep voice and his half-swallowed New Zealand vowels.

At the bus station, Mammy puts tinfoil sandwiches into our carry-on. 'Ham, Noelle. With the good bread, the skull's fresh yesterday.' She takes out her mildewed bottle of Holy Water, shakes it all over us. 'For journeys,' she says to John solemnly. 'Our Lady of Fatima. Now, safe travels.' Never will she say goodbye, she's stubborn about it.

I say 'Get home and go into bed for yourself now, crazy lady.'

They stay and wave till we pull out onto the road to Dublin.

Eighteen

We're at the radiology clinic, across from the obstetricians. Mammy passed on her attachment to doctors – I want someone in a white coat, with a medical degree, monitoring my cervix. And when the moment is at hand, I don't want to be far from an epidural.

The room is dark, a thin bar of summer sunshine slicing through the gap at the top of the curtain. Being in a dark room in the middle of the day makes me think of sex, suddenly. I take my dress off, feeling guilty, as though the nurse might intuit my thoughts and judge me. But she just makes small talk about her family connections in Ireland, as I lay myself awkwardly out on the bed, the paper crinkling beneath my bottom. I can feel, rather than see John behind me at the head of the bed. The gel is cold on my belly. The room is full of the sound of rushing water suddenly, and then, a steady thump that pleases the technician.

'A wee girl.' The man says it right at the end, so the surprise will be better. My heart sinks. I feel a shaming disappointment in the pit of my belly. Not far from where she's lying, probably.

'A girl! A girl!' John's face breaks open in a big smile that looks genuine. 'Fantastic,' he says, pulling me close to him.

'Yay,' I say, feeling like I was winning a race and now I'm coming in second. We smile and thank the man profusely. It's funny, the pressure to perform that comes over you – as though this is the sonographer's choice, and your validation of it is important.

We'd talked beforehand about whether we wanted to know, or whether we should wait. In the end, it was John who forced it. 'I don't want you convinced it's one thing, and then being shocked when it's the other,' he said. I said fine, serenely. I didn't tell him I knew already.

I've been dreaming about a baby boy since I found out I was pregnant. A little boy with blond hair, and dark eyes. Every day recently, I go down to the baths to swim and I close my eyes and he's there with me. I walk down to the edge of the pool, keeping my towel wrapped around me until the last moment. I lower myself down the ladder, grateful for the cover of the cool water. I don't look properly pregnant yet, just a bit lumpy. I let the water hold me up, slice my arms open and shut, gliding very slowly from one end to the other. The light bounces off the white tiles, blue below me and above me. Blue for a boy. All this time I've been quietly certain.

'Oh, everyone thinks she's having a boy the first time,' a friend of ours says laughingly a few months later. I feel momentarily outraged. But it was! I want to tell her. I knew he was there. I knew what he looked like, I'd seen him, with his dark eyes and solemn expression, in a photo of John that his mother gave me. He's two or three, in kindergarten in Wellington, sleeves rolled up to his chubby elbows, staring with intense concentration into a basin of water. I've known that I was having a son who looked like this, ever since the doctor confirmed I was pregnant, the day after Donald Trump was elected. I sat on the crest of the hill in the Auckland Domain, looking down over the Waitematā Harbour, listening to my voicemail. I breathed out into the big blue sky that rolled out ahead of me and felt calmly victorious. For all we'd said we wouldn't mind either way, I'd surprised myself by wanting a baby.

The month before I met John, I wrote a list in the back of a notebook: famous women who don't have children. It was a short list, I'd only started it. Jennifer Aniston, Jane Austen, PJ Harvey. I'd been thinking about all the things I wanted in my life – books, and time, and work, and travel – and also thinking, having a child might be dangerous. Any child I'd have might be like me, like Mammy – and further back, like Han, or Nana.

'Penny for them?' On the way home I'm quiet. He's noticed.

'I'm just thinking: nearly nap time!' Yawning to prove it. I'm thinking about the feel of Mammy's hair in my fingers, how I used to tear it, the yank of it, the squealing. A girl. A girl. It stretches out in front of me.

'You and your snoozing! Champion effort.' He grins. For the last few weeks, I've lost whole afternoons to sleep, a curtain of senselessness that drops every day at 2 o'clock promptly.

'It's a blessing, really, you're not doing the show this year,' he says, but gently. The summer radio show I have done for a long time was scrapped summarily. Hell hath no fury like a woman who got used to all sorts of fortuitous breaks in New Zealand media. How could I have kept my job when I was so chaotic I was drunk in the gossip pages regularly, and lose it now that I am six years in recovery?

I downloaded a period tracker. It beeped one weekend in Martinborough, when we were visiting John's mother. I knew

I was pregnant about a week later. My jeans wouldn't fit me, everything in my body felt burpy and fizzy. I bought a pregnancy test, flicking my head around at the cash register to make sure nobody saw me. Like I was 16 and watching for Daddy, and not a respectably engaged woman of 37. When I came out of the bathroom, it was evening. John was walking around the kitchen, wrapped in the plaid picnic blanket he wears rather than putting on the heating. I waved the stick at him, the blue line visible. We hugged for a second, dazed by the magnitude of it, the majesty of new life in the offing, and then he made steak sandwiches.

'Are you really happy? About her being a girl?' I don't know why I'm asking. It's not him I'm worried about. He has an older daughter he gets on great with, in Paris.

'Of course I am. It's easier in a way, dads and daughters, I know from Chloé. What about you though?' I look at him. He knows me.

'Ah, I am.' And that's not a lie. The baby is the baby. She is mine. I love her. 'It's just . . .'

Standing in the hall, braced against her, smell of Carling, White Linen. She's straining, soft grunts as she tries to keep her balance, hands outstretched, trying to scratch me. 'Go on, do it, why don't you?' Pouring the naggin of Smirnoff down the sink in front of her. 'You little fucking bitch.' Slapping her face as hard as I could. Enjoying it.

'I think it's just a bit harder for me, you know? Mammy and all that.' I'm close to tears suddenly, ridiculously ashamed of myself. One chance, one job and I blew it.

•

Mammy sends me a package. A set of white plastic glow-in-the-dark rosary beads and a thin blue card saying *Our Lady of Childbirth, Augustinian Devotion* with a silver Miraculous Medal wound around it. The medal is on a baby-blue string of cotton and the card has a smiling Mary holding a barefoot, bald Jesus toddler. There are three prayers inside: Prayer for the Gift of Motherhood, Prayer of an Expectant Mother, and Prayer of Thanksgiving, for when it is all over.

'Aren't they lovely?' Mammy is delighted with herself when I call her. 'I got them from the people down in Daunt Square, you know the ones there every day with the big statue of Our Lady? I mean, God love them, they're crazy, but I was looking for a medal for you for ages.' Then, when I am less than enthusiastic about wearing it: 'Shut up, Noelle – that's your Blessed Mother, put on the medal!'

Also in the package is a flimsy pink-and-blue booklet, held along the spine with sellotape, the paper stained in places. The cover says ST FINBARR'S MATERNITY HOSPITAL over a grainy picture of The Holy Family. She says 'They put them next to our beds in St Finbarr's. Every one of us got one.' The booklet is 25 pages long, full of prayers mostly. 'Thanksgiving after delivery.' 'For loved ones at home.' 'Dedication to Mary.'

'What are you laughing at?'

'Prayers Mam, prayers. That's what they give you when you're having a baby!'

'So what? That's lovely.'

'It's useless.'

'Go 'way Noelle, you'll go to hell!' And then, primly: ''Twas a comfort to know the Lord was with me.'

'Good for you, I'd rather an epidural.'

'Oh you're very smart, aren't you? Now, Sarah showed me that photo. Are you sure you've got your dates right? You're very big already.'

I hang up on her, furious. What was my sister doing, showing that Instagram post of me standing beside the big dam in Kurow, with my flowy purple dress and my big belly? We were road tripping down South. I know social media is lame, but I wanted to tell people. And now here's Mammy, sticking her nose in, speculating about my body with a know-it-all tone that brings on the familiar skin-crawl of rage and intrusion. Her drunk eyes on me, trying to get into my life when she has no right to be in there. When it's 4 o'clock in the day and she's drinking already.

I stop talking to her for a while after that, stop taking calls no matter how often she rings me. I know she's desperate when she starts leaving drunk voice messages again, she'd given up doing that years ago. And then one day, I wake up in the early morning with the new ache of my hips spreading and realise that I am safe here, safe in New Zealand. She can say what she wants about my pregnancy, drink what she wants, ring who she wants, but she will only ever be able to see my baby if and when I say so. I start ringing again, on Sunday evenings, but I never let on it's a girl we're having, and I tell her the wrong due date. These details I hoard against her, greedily.

Nineteen

The doctor hits a button over my bed and the room is full of a long, loud clanging that brings people running. John's expression changes from mild boredom to concern, and then alarm, as he's pushed back from me. I can feel a collective sense of urgency that's connected to the numbers rising on the monitor attached to the rise of my belly, but it's difficult to relate any of this to myself and my current situation. I've been lying here for the last five hours, staring out the big picture window at the grey expanse of Auckland. I'm drugged at my own request with a catheter inserted, naked apart from a paper gown with my hair clotted on top of my head and various drips feeding into me. Not long ago – I couldn't say how long, time has become a very slippery concept – I became aware of a painful dragging sensation in my lower back. I couldn't actually feel it properly, but I was conscious of a sound coming out of me. The midwife organised a top-up of the epidural when she heard me moaning. Since then

I've been pleasantly disconnected, lying here, watching the rain come down on the needle of the Sky Tower, the same fragment of a poem repeating in my head endlessly, about a dance at the still point of the world.

I read this poem again and again when I first stopped drinking, underlining great long sections to memorise, it was like a prayer to me. But now all I can remember are these bits of it. There was another line from it, maybe, in *The Silence of the Lambs* – not the film, the book. I sent it to John Paul. Clarice says something about learning to sit still, to care or not care. Or maybe that's a different poem, by the same poet? One he wrote earlier? I'm getting mixed up now – it's the drugs, I'll have to ask my brother.

'OK it's time to push now, Noelle. We'll need a push in three, can you do it?' Dr Carolina, our obstetrician, is at the foot of the bed, looking up at me, with her sharp, clever face, in her little cap with the cartoon sheep on it. I pull myself away from Clarice and Dr Lecter.

'Here we go, here we go.' She's loud, but not shouting, keeping eye contact. She stands between the tent of my legs with her back bent and her neck tense. It's a sporting stance, ready for action, with a low centre of gravity. Are you a pitcher or a catcher, Dr Carolina? I think idiotically, and then want to giggle. I'm so stoned, it feels inappropriate.

'OK, on three, biggest push ever – can you do it?' She counts and I take a big suck of air in, fix my teeth, one row firmly on top of the other. On three, I bear down as hard as I can, but towards the back, not the front, of my body. 'You have to do it like you're pooing', my friend told me recently. 'I don't know why they don't tell us but you have to do it like you're shitting.'

I'm still in the push, it is not ending. John is holding my hand with his two hands so tight it will hurt later, standing up on the balls of his feet in that weirdly graceful way he has, for such a tall person. It's low down the sound explodes, out through my pelvis. And I can see it, actually see it in my mind's eye, the white girdle of bone above the baby opening. It's like the pair of shark jaws, all clean with teeth on them, in that book John Paul and I used to go and sneak looks into, when we were small, in Eason's. At the prenatal class a few weeks ago, the facilitator passed around a smooth grey plastic pelvis for everyone to play with. When she wasn't looking, I took the little plastic baby she gave us to practise bathing, and stuck it back into the pelvis face down so it looked like it was being swallowed. 'You're so disgusting,' my sister texted when I sent her the photo. 'Imagine what it's going to do to me when it comes out, Sarah.'

'She's here. She's here,' John says to me, and I say to John, elated as believers at the Second Coming. The tears are in his eyes, crinkling up at the sides. 'She's here,' he says, gripping my hand with a hitch in his chest, and we're on screen now, in a classic movie scene because someone is bringing her to us, putting her in my arms, this tiny, pale, almond-eyed baby. She looks up with black eyes that have already seen the deepest parts of me, have opened and closed to the travelling music of my voice, the thump of my heart, my belly's gurgle. 'I'm going to take you to Barcelona,' I tell her. 'We'll go to Sagrada Familia, I'll show you everything, baby.'

I didn't expect that to be the first thing I thought of when the midwife handed me my daughter. 'It was the drugs,' John says later. 'You were out of it. It was a bit scary.' I was lying there, he said, with eyes like saucers, raving about Gaudí to a bloodstained baby. 'I've never seen you like that, you were like an animal. The look in your eyes was just . . . wow. Even your teeth looked longer.'

I don't ring home until we are safely at Birthcare. We drive there in the dark, through the park that separates it from the hospital, crawling over speed bumps at 20 kilometres. In the back, the baby sleeps in her capsule, John's red cashmere scarf tucked around her. I've already noted her squashed little ears, the faint red scratches on her forehead where the forceps caught her. The vicious little stab of guilt I felt, touching them gently, is new and familiar already. The nurses cheer in whispers when John rolls me out of the lift in the wheelchair. On the counter, there is a little pile of tiny woollens in pastel colours – peach, white, pale blue, lightest purple – on a wicker tray beside the paperwork. 'For the preemies,' the receptionist says when I touch them quizzically. 'They need the warmth, in the winter.'

In the room, I dial Mammy first, even though I want to call my sister. Before I even say anything, she's wailing. 'Oh my God, oh God bless!' I have to shout over her, 'She's here, Mammy, she's here! You have a granddaughter.' I'm purring like my cat Wildcat, when she had her kittens in the wardrobe. 'Oh God bless her, God bless her.' Mammy's sobbing now, really crying properly. 'Oh Noelle, Noelle! Thank God and his blessed Mother!' She goes on like this for a while, and then hands the phone to Sarah.

'Are you all right?' my sister says, sounding quiet and awed, like the lovely child she was when we were small and I used to mock her. I smirk and say, 'Yes, I'm fine. I'm fine, and so's my daughter.' Years later, when we are walking up to the Mercy, where Mammy is dying several floors above us, Sarah says the words back to me, reminding me of details I've forgotten.

'And then you said her full name: Eve Alexandra Hero Daniell.'

'And what did ye think?' I say.

'Well, Hero, Noelle, come on. What sort of name was that to give her?'

I'd wanted Hero for her first name, but John wouldn't let me. Too much to live up to, he said. Alexandra was his choice, I said it was too horsey. Eve was the only name we could agree on, strong and old and simple. We wrote it out on a piece of paper at the kitchen table just a few minutes before leaving for the hospital, stuck each of our preferred names after it.

'Eve, Alexandra, Hero!' I'm shouting it out for Mammy.

'Hero? What? A Hero? That's not a name.'

'Don't be so stupid, it is a name. It's classical mythology. Ask Robert.'

They hated Eve too, they tell me afterwards. There was an Eve a few doors down from them on the estate, a young child in foster care who had behavioural problems.

'Always tormenting the dog,' Daddy says when I ask about her. 'She'd be at Jenny every time you passed her, poking her with sticks, all that.' 'Eve! Leave that dog alone!' Robert used to shout at her. Sarah does an impression, falls about laughing.

'That's who you named your daughter after.'

Mammy heard my song playing, she always says, when she came out of labour. Like labour is a place you go, which I suppose it is, really. 'The First Noel', that's where they got my name from.

Growing up, I thought Christmas was for me. As soon as the lights were hung up in the city centre, I started my own twinkling. I never felt anything other than special, having a birthday at Christmas, that was a gift Mammy gave me. She never once doubled up on the presents either, I'll give her that much.

It's weird to think of a maternity ward with the radio playing. I can think of nothing worse than having contractions and not being able to change the station.

My parents married in Clogheen church, up the road from where they would build their house a few years later. She carried a long-stemmed white flower – a rose, or a lisianthus maybe. For their honeymoon they got the bus out to Blarney with their luggage. Then they came home and Daddy told his parents. They were 23 years old. He was poor, from the Northside, out of school since age 11. She was twice pregnant already. And then, a year almost to the day later, her arms around the first baby she could keep. Christmas Day in St Finbarr's Hospital.

The first Noel, the angel did say
Was to certain poor shepherds in fields where they lay

My father came to see her with a black eye and a pot of yellow flowers. Someone had taken exception to him smoking a cigar in the pub down by Murphy's brewery. 'Chrysanthemums,' she said. 'I always hated them.'

When Eve is about three hours old, John goes home and leaves us at Birthcare. The bed won't fit him. There aren't that many nearly-seven-foot mothers. One of the nurses comes in and helps me lie Eve in the little wooden cot beside me. Once she's gone, though, Eve starts crying quietly. I look over at her, windmilling one of her arms in the air, fingers covered with a tiny white mitten. I'm struck by the wrongness of being separate from each other. A few hours ago, she was inside me. I reach over and bundle her back up against my shoulder. I lie there, in the soft dim light, with a baby in one arm and the phone in the other. I send John Paul a photo of the baby and tell him what we've called her.

He sends back lines from *Paradise Lost*:

. . . to give thee being I lent
Out of my side to thee, nearest my heart,
Substantial life, to have thee by my side
Henceforth an individual solace dear

At some point in the night, Eve starts coughing. The stuff
that comes up is black, and I panic. I can't work the code on
the phone beside the bed to call a midwife, so I push the alarm
button. The woman when she comes is very grumpy. She explains
there's no emergency, the stuff coming up is meant to be expelled.
I say the colour is frightening and try to make a joke of it, but
she wraps the baby back up and says leave her where she is and
don't push that button again unless it's an emergency. I do push
it again though, because Eve keeps coughing. When the nurse
comes back, she's quite furious. Your baby is wet. You need to
change her, she scolds me, and then tells me off for taking too
long doing it. 'Baby is cold, you need to go faster,' she tuts, sliding
the tiny nappy under her more precisely, doing up the sticky tabs
I've been struggling with. Could you give me a break? I feel like
saying, I've never had a baby before, and I'm coming down off a
shit-ton of fentanyl. But I'm scared Eve will cough again, and the
nurse won't come back if I'm rude to her, so I just say thank you.

I shuffle into the toilet to change the large sanitary pad I put
on earlier, have a flashback to Mammy and her Stayfree. I sit
down and underneath me is raw when the urine flows out of me.
I'm overwhelmed suddenly, by pain and tiredness. I hope the
baby won't cry again, I don't know what to do if she does. I think
about ringing John, but he is very tired too, and he probably
won't know what to do either. I go back and hoist myself onto
the bed beside the little wooden cot. I can feel that I am bleeding
between my legs, warm and wet, or else I have managed to
urinate on myself. Either way, the sensation is lowering. I take

a gulp of the too-sweet orange juice that was brought in for me earlier. And then I remember a woman at work saying that at Birthcare, you can have a toasted sandwich whenever you want one. I pick up the phone, work out the right code this time, and I ask, disbelievingly, if I can have a cheese toastie. Just cheese, or cheese and tomato? the voice asks nicely. Just cheese, I say – but could I have a cup of tea too please? I add, emboldened.

Sure, we'll bring it along, the voice says. It doesn't sound at all cranky. I put the phone down, and sit up straighter. I feel like I've been kicked by a horse in the vagina, and I'm coming down off ten Es simultaneously. But I also have cheese on toast en route to me. I rock the cot softly.

Twenty

'What's she doing now?'

'Not much, just sleeping, feeding.'

'Ah they sleep the day out, don't they, God bless us.'

'Yeah, she's a champion sleeper all right,' I say proudly, adjusting the soft warm weight against me.

'Did you do the bath, like I told you?'

'Shut up about the bath, Mam.'

'Go away girl, I told you – salt, just salt off the table, pour in all of it, and very hot water. Make it scalding. 'Tis great healing – for underneath.' She drops her voice on the last word, like she always did with me and Sarah.

'Stop talking to me about that, or I'll hang up on you.'

'You're so odd, Noelle, you'd bite the head off anyone. I was just saying, the bath is very good, ask John to run it, can't you –'

'I mean it, Carol – leave it.'

'For God's sake!' But she subsides, muttering. The conversation moves on to other things, like how many nappies the baby filled yesterday. Since we came home, about a week ago, Mammy has been ringing every morning. I'm still getting used to it, having traditionally refused to take any calls from her after about 5pm Irish time. But she's sounded sober all this week, or maybe I'm too zonked to notice?

For the first few weeks at home with the baby, John and I sleep separately. He's downstairs in our bedroom, getting up very early for work. I'm sleeping upstairs, in the big sleigh bed our friends who we're renting this house from left us, the baby in a basket next to me. The baby spends minimal time in the basket, being nobody's fool already. We spend hours just lying there, lost in one another, in the big bright room at the top of the house, that's full of cards and presents and a wilderness of flowers. We wash her in a basin on a table next to the bed, checking the water carefully with a rubber-duck thermometer. John is the best at this, fitting the whole of her in the palm of his hand, waving her gently to and fro in the water, singing her songs, with her little babygro on his head, for some reason, while he does it.

I make playlists for night feeds, full of Mazzy Star and Sarah McLachlan and Natalie Merchant. The song I sing her most is On the Street Where You Live, from *My Fair Lady*, the Vic Damone version. I download audiobooks of Sherlock Holmes stories, but I can't concentrate on them, my brain is too fuzzy. I just lie there in the nights, mostly, looking out the window in the lamp-ringed darkness, watching the Sideshow Bob silhouette of the big banana palm in the neighbours' backyard, waving crazily. We are in the teeth of winter. Cold is my dread, in the big old house with the high ceilings. I have two heaters standing one on either side of the bed, and I keep them running. John finds me lying there every morning, topless and sweating, breasts swollen with new milk, basking like a reptile in the artificial heat of the bedroom, baby next to me.

'You must give her fresh air too!' Mammy says, alarmed, when I tell her about the heaters. 'They need fresh air to grow, it's good for them!'

'It's the middle of winter here, I'm not taking her out in that, don't be crazy!'

'Lie her down on a sheepskin, that's what you do, and let her get a bit of sunshine on her bottom.'

'I'm not putting her in a draught.' Later, though, I think vitamin D might not be such a bad idea – in fact, she does have little red spots on her bottom.

The next morning, I lie on my belly and put the baby on her back on a thick blanket in a puddle of sunshine in front of the window. I even crack it an inch or two until a draught blows in, and I bundle her up and take her back to bed again quickly.

Mammy rings then, and tells me about her own mother going into the river. I need a second to process this – both my grandmothers, their insistence on wading into rivers. 'She came out again then,' she says, matter-of-factly. 'She was afraid a neighbour would see her.'

We've been talking about my Granda, how he used to wheel Mammy about as a newborn. Han was depressed, Mammy says, after she had her. 'How do you know?' I say, 'You said she never spoke to you.'

'Ah, everyone knew that, Noelle,' she says crisply. 'Don't be so stupid. She went in, it must have been December, but she came out again, and then she went in to have me, in the Mater. They gave her the gas, that time, she was one of the first to have it. And sure, she was bad then, afterwards, my poor Dad used to have to take me out in the pram after he came in from work, God help us.' The God help us is tender. My saintly Granda, he of the sanctified Mass card on top of the telly.

'She had postnatal depression so, did she?'

'Ah they wouldn't have had the words for it, that time. They moved up to Dublin, she missed her sisters terrible.'

Hannah Mariah, my grandmother, in a black-and-white photo next to Granda's Mass card. Smiling, with a glass in her hand, in a restaurant in Spain. Cigarette in one hand, lively eyes, bright lipstick and dangly earrings. Granda, tanned and handsome, next to her, always.

Maybe everyone thinks it about their granddad, but mine seems to radiate good humour and decency. The big smile that stretched from one cheek to the other, the full head of hair combed back off his forehead with Brylcreem. I can smell it when I think of him, strong and clean and chemical, the earliest smell of manliness I remember. He used to hold my hand the whole way through Mass every Sunday. I tried to stay as quiet as possible, so that when we were released and flowed down the grey stone steps of the Cathedral in the cold bright sunshine with all the others, I'd say, 'Was I good, Granda?' And he'd say, 'Were you good? By the hokey, of course you were!' He taught me how to make China toast, blackening the sliced bread over the blue gas ring, spreading the singed top with melting butter.

Granda knew when Mammy was pregnant again, with the little boy that was born on Good Friday. There she was, in her tiny flat, still working, no boyfriend, no husband – wearing her long poncho around the city, her belly swelling beneath it – determined to keep this one. He went to see her every evening. Stolen hours, between leaving work at the car factory and going home for his dinner. He kept the secret from his wife – whom he adored, according to everyone. He brought a cup of tea to her in bed every morning for half a century.

One day he went to Mammy's flat after work, and it was empty. The neighbours said she'd been taken to the hospital, St Finbarr's. She was in labour. It was too early. 'She may not survive the night,' the doctors told him. Granda Bob had to decide whether to tell my grandmother. What if Carol died and her mother never even knew she was pregnant? What if she didn't, and he was revealed as having kept the secret? Either way, he was in trouble. In the end, he told Han. She refused to go to the hospital.

Shame was a force powerful enough to obscure the humanity of the two people dying that night in a bed in St Finbarr's Hospital. My mother, up in her stirrups, would by no means have been the only young, unmarried woman to die in childbirth and have it be seen as a blessing. Han lived on Chapel Hill, in the shadow of the North Cathedral, seat of the diocese. If she turned her face from her daughter, as she laboured close to dying, she was not alone in doing it.

Mammy didn't die. The baby died. He lived for 11 hours, he had long, perfect fingernails. She told my sister the nurses dressed him up in a sailor suit to bury him.

A sharp pull on my breast as the baby sniffs out the nipple. I stroke the fuzzy down at the top of her head, sliding over the terrifying gap in her skull where the bones have yet to knit together. 'I'd say Han was depressed all right, if she walked into the river.'

'I don't know what she had, I mean, she did I suppose, but she wouldn't have called it that. That time, you didn't say anything, that was private business.'

'Private business!' I snort. 'She needed fucking SRIs and a therapist.'

'She was bad all right,' Mammy concedes. 'It was my Dad who named me. He said, we'll call her Caroline, so, will we? She just said, I don't care what you call her.' She's talking to herself now, more than anyone.

I want to tell her then, about the study I read about baby monkeys. The ones that don't get touched and cuddled as much, don't grow as well, physically or mentally. But I just say, 'Well you love the name Caroline, so that's something.' I don't mention that when we brought Eve home, I couldn't stop crying. It started in the car on the way back, when she was squirming in her capsule. I couldn't bear it. 'Let me help her! Let me help her!' I was howling, crying to John to pull the car over. I tucked her in with the red scarf wrapped more tightly around her, tears dripping down my nose and onto the bundle. When we got back to the house, I refused to stay downstairs until the fire was going. I retreated to the room upstairs, demanded John find the two heaters, crank them up and keep them going. Later, when he made dinner, we had the baby in her bassinet in the middle of the table, but I grabbed her and marched back upstairs when I thought I saw my breath fogging.

'You don't get it!' I screamed when he tried to get me to finish eating. 'You don't understand, what if she isn't warm enough?' And broke down sobbing. 'You don't understand, you can't understand. I'm her mother!' I screamed until my knuckles were white on the handle of the bassinet, poleaxed and terrified by her utter vulnerability, her complete dependence. I took her back upstairs in the end, just lay on the bed and cried, watching that open skull-spot fluttering as she slept on my belly.

'So what happened to Han?'

'I don't know what happened to her. I mean, she was grand, she had more children after that – Uncle Bob, Uncle John. That's what you did then.'

'I hope she picked you up, eventually.'

The baby nuzzles the breast, disgorges the nipple. I pick her up and switch her. She turns her head, making her little kitten noises, stares at me with her deep-set eyes, dark blue with crinkly edges like her father's.

'I think her eyes will stay blue,' I tell Mammy.

'God bless her, like John Paul's,' she says. 'No one knew where he got them.'

I think about how she looked when the midwife brought her over, blood-slick and caked in white scruff like she'd been lapped by the surf and the salt had dried on her. I don't remember her crying at all, just perfect quiet and the shock of her aliveness.

She lies on her front still, to sleep, with her bum in the air like she was in my body, folded up neatly along her own edges. When I sent them that first photo of her, on the big ugly weighing scales in the delivery room, Sarah sent back a photo of one of Mammy's glass angels a few seconds later. Len gives her the angels for her birthday, Mammy is scared of them because they are faceless – 'They freak me'. But she can't tell Len this, so she just takes them and puts them all up high on a shelf where she can't see them. The angel Sarah sends is in the same pose as my baby, crouched on its stomach, sleeping, glass wings folded along the ridge of its spine, neatly.

'I've to go away now. I'm heating up a dinner for Robert.'

'He can get his own dinner, he's nearly 30.'

'You have your own now Noelle, you won't be long seeing they are your child forever.'

A few weeks later, she sends a parcel of photos. Han my grandmother with her sisters and their children, standing outside a farmhouse. The back of the photo says it's a wedding in Kerry. Black-and-white faces, none of them mean anything. I hear

Mammy's voice. She missed her sisters terrible. Bad enough to go into a river at nine months pregnant? There's another photo of Han, elegant as a film star in a neat two-piece, with open-toed espadrilles and a big straw hat, holding the hands of her two eldest, Len and Auntie Cay.

'She was good in her own way,' Carol says when I ring her.

'No she wasn't.' I tuck the tiny baby beneath my chin like a cat with a kitten, cover my vast breasts with my pyjama top, sit upright, incensed by her wishful thinking.

'You know she wasn't. She was a fucking bitch to you all your life, and now you're telling me she didn't even *hold* you when you were a newborn. Can you imagine?'

My eyes fill with tears involuntarily. It's the hormones. I move the small weight onto my shoulder, feeling a gentle escape of air from the back of her nappy.

'Ah sure, she was sick. And there was no help for women those days.'

'Well, it sounds like she was carrying some fairly hefty suicidal tendencies.' I'm trying to sound ironic, but my legs are out in goosebumps in the overheated bedroom. The shock of cold water. The stink of the canal. What sent her wading in there? Three young children at home, and a new baby in her belly. It was 1953. Pope Pius XII in the Vatican, his picture in every Catholic kitchen. Did she want another baby? What else could she do if she didn't? Down to the canal, on a black evening around Christmas. And then Mammy, twenty years later, coming down on that train from Dublin, her arms empty. My eyes are full of tears, the baby pressed against me.

'Go on so, have a sleep, I'll be on tomorrow.'

Twenty-one

'Don't touch him! You broke the last one.'

I'm standing in front of the old Hi-Fi unit in the front room in Hollymount, against the wall closest to the bookshelves, next to the big front window. Over the years, as the technology has been supplanted, the unit has slowly morphed into a place where everything ends up: piles of Johnny Cash CDs we bought for Daddy, ugly ornaments, bottles of weird drink the neighbours brought back from Bulgaria.

I have my hand on the crib, which stays up all year round in Mammy's house, where Christmas is a religion. I'm reaching out to touch a wise man, I don't know how she can see me. 'I wasn't doing anything to him, just looking at your madness.'

She's standing in the archway of the kitchen, where she's been making ham sandwiches. 'Go 'way, you broke the last fella. One of ye did anyway, the head's gone off him.'

'Well, you have two more.'

'There were three of them, Noelle.' She points a buttery knife at me. 'You're very awkward, you. Leave him alone. Don't touch anything.'

I follow her out to the kitchen, shifting the baby from one shoulder to the other. Nine weeks old. Still light, but getting heavier.

'Lie her down on the sofa, will you? She'll have that arm worn off you'.

'No, she's fine, she wants to have a look around.' I bring her over to the kitchen window, where the sun is pouring in, bathing the Busy Lizzie.

'Now come in here, I want you to have a proper look at the stuff I bought her.'

I suck down a big heavy sigh. The sofa at the back of the front room, where the Christmas tree goes usually, is completely full of stuff she's bought for Eve. Useless stuff mostly. Half the room is covered in toys, bears, blankets, books; there is even a toy pram to push and dolls to put into it. I tried to explain about luggage yesterday but she waved me off – Mammy doesn't give a shit about baggage allowance. When we walked in yesterday, still jetlagged, the spread was dazzling. It looked like a toy shop. Only when you got up close could you see most of the things were slightly ragged around the edges. Chips on the plastic counting games, little patches of baldness where the fur was stuck together on the pink-and-white teddies. The books, I knew, would have other children's names in them. And then there were the things that were out of their era, like the multicoloured baby sling with instructions on a DVD.

She held it up again, 'Isn't that gorgeous, like the one you have only nicer? And you'll be able to see all the ways to put her in it, in the video.'

'And where'll we get a DVD player?' I ask sourly.

'Sure there'll be one in the place ye're staying,' she says airily. 'Ring down to reception.'

'We're staying in a hotel, Carol, not an electronics shop in the 1990s.'

She isn't listening, she's disappeared into the utility room. She comes back out, bent under the weight of something so big it obscures the top half of her body.

'What the fuck is that?'

'Ah look at her Noelle, isn't she gorgeous?'

It's a statue, gold painted, of a native American woman. There is a feather in her hair and a cape around her shoulders. Her bright red lips are kissing the baby she is holding. I look at it, speechless. ''Tis a pity it's a boy,' she says musingly, 'the child, like. That's the only thing.' She stands it upright. It's about the size of a decent tombstone.

I stare at it, the room spinning. Eventually I say, 'I'm not taking that back to New Zealand.'

She looks at me contemptuously. 'Ah grand so, after I dragged it down the North Main Street for you.' She levers it up, pulls it over and sits it on the marble fireplace, beside the china dolls on an ornamental bench and last year's reindeer. The woman looks out at us, cradling her baby. 'Take it now, if you want it,' she offers, when she catches me staring at it.

'Come and look at this,' she says then, not giving up on me. Some kind of plastic game for two players with brightly coloured fish and two big levers.

I indicate the sleeping infant on my chest. 'She's not even three months old, Ma.'

'Well she'll grow up! Won't she!'

Suddenly I'm angry. One of the levers on the game is jammed, some of the fish have fins missing. The spine is cracked on the book next to me. Why is she buying all this shabby old shit for my baby? All these things, full of the drool and germs of all the children who had them before us? 'Why did you buy all of this' – I swipe my arm across her sofa – 'when you know we can't take it back with us? It won't fit in a suitcase!'

She glares at me, down either side of her pointy nose, and I know my face is red, I'm so furious. I wrap my arms around my sleeping child in her flower-print muslin, hot waves of anger rolling off me. 'You bought all this crap, and we can't take it back, it's USELESS.'

She narrows her eyes, purses her lips. 'Ah you needn't take them so, go on away, so, girl.'

Next to me on the sofa, there's a big blonde doll, bigger than the baby on my lap, that's just like the one I had when I was small. Beside it, a red ball with cut-outs to fit a bag of plastic shapes through. On the floor, in the pram, a little pile of fairy stories – all my favourites, *Sleeping Beauty*, *Rapunzel*, *The Musicians of Bremen*, all with the beautifully illustrated covers I remember. All my favourites, from the Hospice Shop, the St Vincent de Paul, the Cystic Fibrosis. It would have taken her weeks to put it all together.

She goes out through the kitchen and I hear a window opening. I am filled with a cold sense of disappointment as I feel my heart rate slowing. Some women have mothers who come and stay with them after they have their babies – who clean the house, and make dinner and do the washing. Mothers to talk to about breastfeeding and nappy rash and reflux. I look down and see she's put two giant bars of Cadbury Whole Nut chocolate into the toy buggy. Not just family size, even bigger – I've never seen a bar of chocolate that size in New Zealand. I go out into the kitchen, where she's leaning over the window ledge. She rubs the fag on an ashtray when she sees me coming with the baby.

'I'm sorry,' I say, 'they're lovely. You're so good to buy her all the presents. Maybe they can stay here, and she can play with them every time she comes? That can be the playroom.'

She looks at me. 'That's where the Christmas tree goes. But we'll see, sure. And she'll have to have more stuff anyway, as she gets older.'

We are not christening the baby, but they want a party anyway. 'Sure you have to give people a night out,' Daddy says, 'they'll only talk about you otherwise.' I say no. John says 'Where's the harm in it? A few drinks, to celebrate, for your relatives. It's a big deal for them too, you know – she's the first grandchild.'

The hotel I like, down by the river, will do canapés for thirty, but it's too expensive. In the end, Daddy picks the place. Another new hotel – it used to be the North Infirmary – just down from the Cathedral.

We're a few minutes late pulling up, John reaches me out of the taxi. I stumble, all my weight's in front with the baby pack. I've made an effort, with low heels and make-up. Mammy's out in the carpark, smoking, agitation radiating off her. 'Come on, Noelle – where were ye? They're waiting!' She makes a furious chopping gesture in the air with her hand to shoo us towards her. My blood pressure goes up just looking at her. She's had a few already. Why are we even doing this? She's always the same. My stomach twists, I'm going to hate it.

'Come on so, Carol.' John goes up and links his arm through hers. I can't help laughing whenever they line up together, she only comes up to his navel.

Inside, Robert leans against the bar, watching everything. 'I don't know why she's here,' he nods at Carol, who is smiling tight-lipped at various relatives. 'She hates people. A misanthrope, Noelle.'

'Stop showing off, I know what a misanthrope is, Robert.'

'Hello niece,' he says, dropping an air kiss onto the sleeping baby. 'I'm going outside now.' Stepping around me delicately, a pint and two longneck bottles of Coors gathered chest height to his body. 'Father gave me his box of fags to mind, which was a miscalculation on his part. I'll have you know, I intend to smoke all of them.'

The hotel is surprisingly nice, for a place people used to die in. A long bar along one wall, held up by white pillars. My aunts and my cousins are arranged in their usual formation, three Heaphy sisters in descending order, in front of coolers of white wine, on comfortable patterned sofas. They coo over the baby, fast asleep in the sling tied to the front of me. When I say I don't want to wake her up, Audrey nods approvingly. 'That's right girl, don't give her to no one. You're always like that with the first one, I was the same with my eldest.' I sit there for a while with them, just laughing and talking. It feels easier for me than it has in decades. Maybe it's the baby? When I was about to go to New Zealand, they had children already. I remember trying to buy Audrey a drink at the bar, that night at the Josh before I went, asking her what she wanted, and she said, 'You don't have to buy us drinks at all, girl, we've fellas and husbands.'

I laugh it off when any of them ask if there's another baby coming. 'Don't leave it too long,' says an aunt passing on her way to the bar. 'You know what they say, an only is a lonely.'

'Don't mind her, do what you want,' says Audrey, tapping my wrist and locking eyes with me. I nod, like when I was small and I worshipped her, doing whatever she told me. 'One is grand, sure you can travel the world with her.'

There are people here I haven't seen in decades, all relatives. Everyone has brought something, even though I told Daddy to say no presents. I'm buried in gift bags within the first five minutes – pink mostly, with unicorns on them, and Disney princesses. Every time an uncle comes down from the bar, another Ballygowan is put in front of me. I can't find John, he's probably outside smoking with Robert.

I sit and watch Mammy – she's relaxed slightly, talking to one of her favourite cousins, a man with curly red hair who used to play in a band when we all went on holidays in Kerry. He never drank alcohol, which marked him as unusual. I remember him, standing on the low stage of the big hotel looking out over the waves in Glenbeigh, blue spotlights playing over his face, as he downed a pint of fizzy orange, sweat running down his face, his guitar strapped around him. Thirty years later, and there's another pint of fizzy orange in front of him. Mammy is leaning forward, captivated by whatever he is telling her – gossip, probably, from the village where we used to go. He still has a house below there, knows all the comings and goings, who's getting planning permission from the County Council.

I watch Mammy, confident she won't see me. Her pink hair is bright, she must have done it recently. She was a vision in pink and purple when she met us at the train station, standing on the platform with two big purple balloons with Eve's name on. The balloons looked like they were going to float her off, up high over the roof of the train station. She's lost more weight since we were here last summer. She's a size six now, she told me. In her St Vincent de Paul shop sometimes she gets clothes from the children's section. Tonight she's wearing a smart white coat: '2 Euro from the Cystic Fibrosis.' It's too big for her, makes her look a bit like an orderly. Is this the hospital Uncle John died in? It is. She'll pose outside the window of his hospital room later tonight, out in the carpark, insist we take her photo. He was only 17. Hodgkin's Lymphoma. 'A tragedy has come to our family,' Granda said, the day he died, Auntie Cay told me. I wanted to say to her, What about the baby his daughter had to give away? But I didn't, she said it so reverently. Han didn't last long after John died, either, she said. That's when she went downhill properly.

At some point, while it's still light, outside the big picture windows, I get up to find the Ladies. Walking down a long corridor, Mammy is suddenly ahead of me. 'Come here, come here a minute!' she hisses.

'What? I need to go to the toilet.'

'Just come here, for fuck's sake, will you?' Baring her teeth at me, gesturing furiously.

Inside what appears to be an empty boardroom, there's a long trestle table with an enormous cake on it, a great big slab of a thing, covered in blinding white icing. Four large sugar roses at each corner, WELCOME BABY EVE 7-7-17 in curly purple writing.

'Jesus Christ Mam, are you feeding the five thousand?'

'Shut up Noelle. What do you think? I got purple, you said you don't like pink for her. Isn't it lovely?'

I look at the immense thing in front of us. She couldn't have just gone with flourless chocolate?

'You don't like it, do you?' Voice curdling with disappointment. 'Sure you're always the same, you are.'

I look down at the enormous cake. The baby scratches my breast with her translucent fingernails. She's hungry. 'It's amazing, Mammy. I've never seen anything like it. You're fabulous. Thank you.' I reach over and mark her cheek with a perfect wine-coloured kiss print.

'Ah go away you liar. You think I'm foolish.' Smiling. She reaches into her bag – a burgundy linen tote, gold elephants woven into it – takes out a disposable camera with a cardboard cover, pulls back the little wheel on the top, points it at the cake and snaps a photo.

'Where did you get that? I haven't seen one of those since my confirmation!'

She drops it back in the bag. 'That's my own business. Come on so, is my lipstick on?' baring her teeth again.

'No, you're grand.'

'Come on so, we'll go back in, they'll be talking about us.'

'They'll be talking all right when they see this cake, Mama.'

'It's lovely, isn't it?' Gazing down on it fondly. 'The waitress said she'd bring plates for it.'

I fuss with the straps of the baby pack, Mammy waiting impatiently. 'You're not feeding her again, are you?' Mammy is not convinced breastfeeding is essential, she suspects it is something I am doing for attention. 'I'm going back, so I need a smoke. Stay there you, sure.'

Later on, we all come back into the boardroom where the cake is. My uncle tells funny stories. I whisper to John, 'Should we say something?'

'You go first,' he says. 'I'll follow.'

I stand up, the baby sleeping peacefully on my chest, say something about how meaningful it is for Eve to have her family here tonight, when home is far away for us. 'John now!' shouts Mammy, before I've finished the sentence. 'Let's hear from John now.' She's wedged between some cousins, face glowing, a pint in front of her. The cake was very well received, most people had some. John stands up, says pretty much what I just said, and the cheer at the end is louder than my one. Daddy sings Good To Be Back Home Again, his John Denver staple, doesn't even get up from the table, just pushes the chair out a bit, and closes his eyes like when we were children, and everyone sings along about this old farm feeling like a long lost friend, and my John gets a bit misty-eyed and says, 'This is lovely, actually.' Then my cousin with the red hair stands up and everyone is quiet.

He starts off, low and sad, singing something about a train coming into the station. 'He always does this one, for his mother,' Auntie Cay whispers. His mother is one of Han's sisters' daughters, my mother's cousin Nancy. Cay's in a long flowy caftan, come up from Kerry, where she's been living for the last few years, back in the village they all used to go to on holidays. 'Look at her,' Mammy hissed earlier, throwing her eyes over to where Cay is talking to one of my father's brothers. 'Look at her, talking to everyone! It's unknown what she'll be saying, girl. Nonsense, the usual.'

So come a little closer, put your head upon my shoulder

My cousin's voice fills the room with yearning. His eyes are closed as he sings, moving slowly from one foot to the other. The whole room is swaying now, under the fluorescent lights that haven't dimmed all evening. I pat the baby, swinging her backwards and forwards, and Daddy's next to me suddenly, leading me out into the middle of the floor, in front of the round tables full of all my cousins, sitting back in their chairs, singing softly to each other. Daddy's waltzing me and Eve around in a circle and Mammy's up too now, stepping towards us, in her too-baggy pants and stocky black summer sandals, wiggling her shoulders.

Back and forward we step, Mammy on one side of me, Daddy on the other. Mammy puts her hand around the sling, reaches in and tries to kiss Eve, misses, kisses a spot in the air a few centimetres above her forehead.

And come a little closer, put your head upon my shoulder

Daddy sings along, his voice as rich as it was for John Denver earlier. All of my cousins are clapping for us, I can feel myself blushing.

Let me hold you one more time before the whistle blows

I look over to where John is filming, do an embarrassed wave at him. I'll watch the video again, on a plane a few years later, on my way home to the Mercy. My cousins cheer as Mammy joins us, walking fast into the frame, taking her place beside me, reaching over to kiss the baby. An aunt pops up to take a photo, freezing us in the moment. The aunt disappears, and it's just the three of us with Eve, strutting our little circle on the hexagonal function room carpet – me, Mammy and Daddy and their sleeping granddaughter.

Twenty-two

We walk belly to belly, my arms tight around her. The headlights
are bright eyes in the rain. A light drizzle but thorough, the thin
gauze of my dress is clung to the backs of my legs already. We pass
the Protestant church that got taken over by the Catholics a
few years back, the crazy ones who only say the Mass in Latin,
and strap the cutty things – I can't remember what you call
them – onto the tops of their thighs while they're praying.
The cars crawl down the hill to Sunday's Well as we crawl up it.
She's surprisingly heavy on the upward slope – I haven't been
doing the exercises like John showed me. I tried, before we left
New Zealand, puffing on the dusty floor of the lounge like a
fish flapping out of the water. But what's the point? Since the
birth I've just been lying on the sofa with her mostly, eating like
a horse, wearing the same big dresses to cover my jelly.

She tips me forward as we walk, the sling keeps slipping. I had
to roll her in a muslin this morning, she's still too small to fill it.

We pass the new houses. I was calling them that twenty years ago, when I was walking down past them to college. They're all bright red brick still, all with their own name plates – Tír na nÓg, Dún Rí, Tibidabo. The cars are in a line going up as well as down, there's new traffic lights on the corner. I pull my coat open until the top of her head appears. She's asleep still, breathing easy, one side of her face tilted up towards me. I close the coat quickly. She's new enough still for me to feel a sense of triumph when I can keep her asleep for any substantial period. The briars follow us along the boreen in a creeping, green tangle. The first blackberries are already poking through, hairy and jewel-coloured. I have a sudden flash of the tins we used for collecting: pale-coloured, white or pink with gold tops. SMA baby formula. The nuns gave all the new mothers a drink to dry their milk out, Mammy told me yesterday. God knows what was in it.

When Mammy got pregnant the first time, Han said, 'You better write to your sister. She's going to have a heart attack when you tell her.' Auntie Cay always had a bad heart. But the letter didn't kill her, it brought her home from California. She went with my mother, up to see the child in Dublin. They went to Dunnes Stores first, for baby clothes – 'the best of everything', Auntie Cay said on the night in Jurys, a few years ago, when she told me.

Mammy wouldn't go into the place when they got there. She sat on the wall outside, smoking. 'Count her fingers,' she said. 'Count her toes. Dress her. Talk to her.'

Auntie Cay said the nuns let her hold the baby, and play with her. 'I thought about just walking out the door with her in my arms.' There was a catch in her voice saying it. 'I could have taken her back to America. Mike would have had her, she would have been a sister for Caragh. But I couldn't, you know? Han was so strict, she would never have had it. And your mother would have said "that's my child" every time we came back to Ireland. Of course she would have. It would have been too hard then, for everyone.'

'Is it done?' Granda asked, when they came back down from Dublin. 'The image of *him*, huh?' Han said. Him being some other man, not my father. Some other man who may, or may not, have raped her daughter. 'She is a beautiful little girl,' Auntie Cay says she told her. 'May God forgive us.' It didn't need to have been a scandal, she said, it was the '70s by then already. 'All the cousins who got pregnant after that, they kept their babies. They saw what it did to your mother.'

Across the road, the madhouse is a golf course now, the pitch richly green and perfectly even. Several pale blue hydrangea bushes bloom at orderly intervals. St Anne's, or Our Lady's, I'm never sure which was the hospital, and which was the asylum. She worked there until I was born. When I was small, she would tell us about the patient who whispered to her one night, very softly, 'Nurse Speight, I am going to kill you.' She said the woman's low voice was the most terrifying thing about her, she always did that part carefully. They used to lock them in at night, the patients, inmates. Locked them up in straitjackets. This was as late as the mid-'70s. But maybe I only imagined that? Maybe she only said it to scare me. We used to drive in there, to drop off carloads of kittens. 'They'll be grand,' my dad would say, watching as they disappeared into the long grass. 'Plenty of food in the woods for them.'

I check my phone. It's still very early. John was still fast asleep when we left, the jetlag is brutal and he had a few drinks at the fake christening. I'm not sure they'll even be awake when we get there, but I decide to keep going. I left the house on a whim – since the baby was born, I've started snatching at even the tamest adventures.

We wait until the cars pass, to cross over the road opposite the Crucifixion statues. Carol always insisted the taxi drivers came home this way, rather than passing the Corporation houses, with their satellite dishes and graffiti. Jesus hangs off the cross, suffocating under his own weight, wearing what looks like rouge and lipstick. Mary, weeping at his feet, done up heavily also. I look up at the spear wound in the side of the dying Christ. This fucking country.

The last stretch of road is lined by trees that were planted when I started primary school, now growing thick and tall on either side of us. The field where I kissed Keith O'Connor and let him put his hands on the back pockets of my jeans is a ghost estate now, the white wires of outside light fittings hanging from empty doorways like veins of something flayed open. None of the windows have glass in them, but apart from an eyeless look, all of the houses are finished and ready. Who did they ever think was going to live here? How did they convince themselves it was a good idea to build them? Money. The last row of houses looks down on the back of the asylum, I know the view from memory.

That was the nurses' block, where they did their training. They haven't pulled it down yet, it's a shell now, after the fire. 'Best thing for that place,' people said. It's hard to disagree once you hear the stories. I remember trying to stand one of her winged nursing caps on my head, but my fingers were too small and fat, the cardboard too slippery to bend it properly. Granda Bob wrote a letter on his deathbed, she said, about what happened to her. She didn't say the word for it then, or maybe she did, and I pretended I knew what it meant, but I didn't.

By the time I reach the gap in the fence, the bundle is stirring. I walk a bit quicker, we're nearly there now. Past the green electricity supply box that seemed so high to jump off. They used to have the bonfires right beside it every summer. For days before, all the boys on the estate would go gathering – branches, clothes, furniture. Someone put a big tyre on there one year as a kind of finale, once it got going. I stood downwind, eating crisps and jellies, thrilled by the greasy shimmer of the air between the flames, the pop and hiss of gases exploding, the billows of chemical smoke blowing over us.

The house is quiet when I push the front door open. I like it like this – morning sun softening all the piles of crap and old photos. Moon-faced me looks down from above the ironing board, 21 with dyed red ringlets and a big flushed face, accepting my degree from some ginger-bearded Chancellor of the University. Inexplicably, I am wearing a pearly green eyeshadow that makes my face look even redder. Fresh cigarette smoke hangs in the air. She's in the front room, at her usual seat, staring out the front window. Her injecting kit and blood reader are on the table in front of her, next to the big John Player Blue ashtray. She looks up and can't hide her delight, stubbing the fag out quickly.

'What brought ye? 'Tis very early!'

'Sure we were awake anyway.' I open my coat, hover my hands above her.

'Ah take her out of that thing you have her in. She'll be too hot altogether.'

I take my coat off, and open the top straps of the carrier. I lift the baby out gently, a seed from a pod. My mother watches hungrily. Eve mewls, big dark eyes drinking in my face. I bask in her focus.

'Good morning,' Mammy sings to her, in the bright voice she uses for the baby only. If she's hungover from last night, you wouldn't notice.

'Good morning to you too, Carol, Car-Car – is that what we're calling you?' I perch on the side of the sofa, along from the full ashtray and discreetly push my nipple above the soft neckline of my dress. Eve clamps down on it greedily.

'God you must be exhausted from it.' Her tone full of admiration and worry.

I lie back on the sofa, frog-legged baby fastened to the front of me, her clean milky smell filling my nostrils, along with familiar smells of home: wet dog and cigarettes and old fried breakfasts. 'It's fine, once I eat plenty.'

'Will I make a slice of toast for you? Or have a biscuit, let you?' There are two full boxes from last Christmas on the kitchen table still, I know without looking. 'Here, I'm having a cream cracker before I do my bloods – take it.' She holds up two crackers sandwiched together, a slice of processed cheese in the middle. She passes it over. I push the top cracker down, feel the little worms of butter oozing through the bottom. I bite down and the cheese coats the back of my teeth, cold from the fridge and sourly plastic. It's delicious.

'I'll make you a cup of tea with it.' She shuffles out in her ugly boxy shoes, polio boots my brother calls them. I remember her saying, you have to be careful of your feet with diabetes.

Eve's asleep again by the time she comes back, with a mug that's stained as brown on the inside as the tea that's in it. I bleached all the cups the last time I lived here, before I went back to New Zealand. My nose wrinkles involuntarily. I need to change the baby. 'Have you a cloth to put her down on?'

I pop the fasteners on the babygro, marvel at her little red legs, perfect and undefended. She's lying on her back on the flowery sofa, on top of a white tea towel that says ALGARVE in curly red letters, a present from the neighbours. Carol leans over her, talking nonsense. Eve is looking up and giggling, maybe at her, maybe at the light fitting. I wriggle a tiny nappy underneath her.

Carol walks over and opens the kitchen window. She lights up, looking back in at us. I re-dress the baby and she closes the window, I hear the tap running. At least she's trying. Sometimes I forget she has nurse training. She comes back in, wipes her hands on the tea towel and I hand Eve to her.

'She's big isn't she? A grand big girl, you are, you are.' Eve looks up at her with her almond-shaped eyes. They are lost in each other.

'She was small, when she was born – seven pounds only. It didn't feel like it, trying to get her out, though. But I had good drugs,' I tell her, proud to have organised it properly.

'I had an epidural, the first time,' she says, looking straight ahead, away from the baby. 'Not with ye, long ago, up in Dublin.'

Under my dress and the nursing slip my body goes cold and then hot all over. I stare out the window, at the trees that were always spindly, until last summer when I came home and they suddenly covered the view out onto the road, thickly and greenly.

She's matter of fact, no bitterness. 'That time, if you were having a baby and you were unmarried, they thought you were a bit simple, a bit retarded. I was in so much pain. My God, the pain, I'll never forget it. So I asked the doctor – the head guy you know, some Dublin consultant. The nurses, the sisters, they'd tell you to shut up, to offer it up, but the gas wasn't working. He came into the room and I said, "Doctor, I'm in agony, please help me."'

She repeats the words carefully, from memory. Her spine straightens as she's telling me. Eve is lying still in her arms, transfixed by the lace around the neckline of her cheap white jumper. 'I asked him straight out. I did. And you never did that, that time. But he looked down at me. "Nurse" – he said – "we'll do an epidural. Get this patient ready."'

There's no eye contact between us, I'm sitting alongside her, but I'm not, really. I'm in a white room, heavy with the smell of fear and disinfectant, in a hospital somewhere in Dublin in the 1970s. The Mater maybe, who knows, could have been Drimnagh. She's in front of me, lying on her side on the bed, long dark hair pouring over one shoulder, naked and swollen. There's a man sitting in front of her, threading his big needle into the tiniest hollow in her spinal column.

'Did it work?' I keep my voice steady, like it's all right to be talking about this, finally. Like the world won't crack and crumble.

'Ah, it did. For a while anyway. But I'll never forget that pain, before it.' Her arms are folded around my baby, a perfect circle. How old was she then – 18, 19? She would have got the train up. Back down again, by herself. Her brother made a joke about an eight-pound kidney stone, or maybe that's a joke I heard about someone else in that situation.

We sit alongside one another on the flowery sofa, an infant, a toddler, a little girl, my sister in the space between us. She went to a family in Belfast, maybe. Vision of a slab-faced nun handing a man and a woman a little white bundle. One photo, only, in the album with sunflowers on the cover, a fair-haired child, in an orange check dress on a snowy carpet – a stranger, not one of our cousins. Crying and screaming every year in the front room, on a day in March, the little girl's birthday. Crying and screaming when she was drinking, only.

Eve starts to fuss, windmilling her fists in the air. She's hungry again. I reach for her. There's a moment where it looks like Carol won't give her up, but then she gathers the baby in her white muslin wrap and kisses her gently on the forehead before handing her over.

Twenty-three

She's had a few, the ends of her words are sliding on top of one another. It's like nails on a blackboard. They only got in an hour ago. The flight was delayed from Dublin.

'Your Dad is very upset. Stop at him, all right? He can't help it. He can't do planes, girl. His nerves are bad, after his mother and everything. Just ring him now, and tell him it's grand, let you. Sure, you've enough people, aren't we all here?'

'Mam –'

'And what a journey! That coach, go away, it nearly killed me. Why you had to get married in the middle of nowhere anyway, Noelle, is beyond me.'

I contemplate telling Mammy to go fuck herself as I intended, but there are two days to get through still, including the wedding.

They hate the holiday park. Little chalets, no frills. Crucially, no off-licence. I tried to explain before they got here that someone should rent a car, if only to go to the supermarket. But Sarah flatly refused to drive on the wrong side of the road with Mammy next to her.

'And the heat!' Mammy's still droning down the phone. 'The butter we brought is melted, the rashers will be gone off.'

'Rashers can't go off,' I say absent-mindedly, swatting a mosquito, thinking about Daddy. 'Bacon is cured, that's the point of it.'

'Oh shut up, Noelle' she says irritably. 'You always know everything, you do. I'm going to bed soon, anyway. I'm exhausted. Sarah and Robert are coming over to ye, for a dinner is it?'

'Yeah, just a small thing.' John's relatives, all the cousins from England. At least they won't have to meet her until tomorrow. Maybe we can hide her somehow.

'I just hope I can sleep in this heat. I'm telling you, my back is killing me.'

I stand still for a second, shut my eyes. The sun's low behind the big orange trees at the end of the garden. On the stone wall, hidden behind the bushes, a peacock calls suddenly, a wild sound, ragged and unlovely. It lives around here, Nathalie the landlady told us, be careful not to let it shit on your beach towels. The last warm rays sink lower in the west, catching my shoulders. We sat outside here this morning, with all the little whirring, chirping bits of garden life stirring, watched Eve cover her naked self in jam from her croissant, laughed and took photos. What's the Talking Heads song again? How did I get here, my beautiful life?

'Good night so Mam, I'll see you tomorrow.'

'Good night so girl, sleep you well.'

Mammy and Len stay up until 11, drinking Mexican beers by the kidney-shaped pool at the holiday park, Sarah tells me the next day.

•

'Jesus Christ, Noelle.' John squints behind his glasses, face flushed from the sun, hair still salty. 'We're getting married in a few hours. Tomorrow this will all be over, and they'll all pile onto a plane back to where they came from. If you don't want Mammy or Sarah or John Paul or Robert to walk you down the aisle, fine – don't do it. Walk yourself down, or fuck it, I'll come get you.'

'No, John, that defeats the purpose.'

'Fine! I don't care. You don't actually care either. You weren't even sure you wanted your Dad to walk you down the aisle. Said it was all patriarchal bullshit –'

'I DO think that. But it's a fucking long walk from that room where I'm getting dressed, to the altar!' The sob in my voice makes me furious. I can't believe Daddy's left me hanging.

When we first said we were getting married in France, he rang to say he'd applied for a passport. 'Perpignan, here we come!' he said in a terrible fake French accent. 'Oooh la la! I looked it up Moll, right there near the Spanish border.' I could see him sitting in the kitchen in Hollymount, the big atlas out on the table in front of him.

'What about the plane, Daddy? Are you sure you can do it?' I'd half thought both of them might skip it. Portugal was the one time they ventured overseas, nearly twenty years back – a holiday low on highlights apart from, somehow, running into a man in the resort who played guitar in a pub in Shandon after my christening.

'Of course we're coming,' Mammy said, affronted. She's the better traveller, after years of going to see John Paul in Oxford.

'How will you do the flying, Dad?'

'Sure, I'll have to, won't I? Unless I want to walk it.'

'I'll get him tablets,' Mammy hissed, when he passed her the mobile. 'Mary next door got valium going to Bulgaria. She said if he takes a couple of them, he won't know what he's doing.'

'Well don't give too many,' I say, alarmed at the prospect of a zombified Daddy roaming the backblocks.

'Shut up Noelle, I'll get him there.'

But she didn't. She's here and he isn't. I can't believe I have to get married without the public-facing parent.

'Look.' John takes a deep breath. 'We can do what we want. That's the point. We're the ones getting married, we're the ones who matter. You, me, and her.' He gives the naked child in his arms a jiggle. She is happily chewing on half a pastry beneath the sun hat Mammy got her in the St Vincent de Paul shop for a euro. 'I mean it though, just get over it, because it's exhausting. I'm going in for a lie down for a bit, I suggest you do the same.'

He walks off, in his orange-and-red sarong, the one that used to cover a bedside table in the first house where we lived together, about 40 minutes from here, towards the mountains. I still have the feeling, a cold black river of certainty running beneath everything, that no matter what happens, eventually he's going to leave me.

I flash back to that moment, a few years ago, standing on a street in Paris, arguing. I'd made him take me to a part of the city he didn't know, miles out of our way because Google said it had a COS store. But the shoes I liked were too small and the clothes were out of season, wrong for going back to New Zealand. I wasn't crying because of that, exactly, but it probably was a precipitating factor. 'I'm sorry,' I said eventually. 'I'm just really sad about leaving, and anxious about going back to New Zealand.' He just stood and watched, didn't comfort me like he usually did. Eventually he said, 'I'm getting a bit bored of you being unhappy constantly.'

I walked off in a haze of fear and fury, sat down in a tourist cafe, and got a plate of ham sandwiches for 25 Euro. Packet ham, on plain white bread, a smear of butter. He found me there, we laughed over the sandwiches, but it's been in the back of my head since then that I'm on borrowed time. I'm too self-centred, too volatile emotionally. If you put a gun to my head right now, and said Do you think he'll go through with it, do you think he'll marry you in front of all our friends and relatives, in a few hours' time – I don't know if I would say yes.

I sit at the little table, drum my heels on the ground in frustration. It doesn't feel right to ask Mammy to walk me down the aisle, that would be false advertising. Sarah is holding Eve, we decided, and I don't want my brothers – I don't like the idea of substituting the men in my family for each other. I sit at the green iron table under the bougainvillea and think about it. About Daddy, how he looks at me with naked pride, as though I can do anything. I think about how I want to move from one stage of my life to the next. I send three texts, get three replies one after the other. And then I go and have a shower.

Before going over to get dressed, I ring Daddy.

'How are you?'

'Era, sure you know, not great. I'm going out with the dog there, now.'

'Wouldn't you go see Thomas, or Walter?' His brothers. 'Don't be alone Dad. I'm sorry you're not here with us.'

'I am too, sure.'

'Listen Daddy, I am all right. I'm sad, but I'm fine. I'm getting married today. I love you.'

'Love you too, Moll, have a great day the two of ye.'

Not long before the ceremony, Eve falls down and scrapes her forehead. I press a cloth to the big scratch, stroke the French dirt out of it gently. She's a soldier when she's hurt, shrugging off discomfort – I think she gets it from her father. But now she cries and cries. The cut is shallow but wide, on the thin skin above her eyebrows, it must be throbbing. I cuddle her tight and bring her down with me when it's time to put my dress on. We are getting married in a place where they used to press wine for vin de table. The ceremony will be under some trees in the main courtyard, where horse-drawn carts used to pull up with grapes to be weighed and sorted. Nathalie has strung fairy lights in the trees for later, we've filled up the horse troughs with bottles of champagne and San Pellegrino.

When I get to the little anteroom at the bottom of the courtyard, the glass doors won't open. Word goes round the compound, nobody knows where the key is, everyone is searching. I peer in through the gap in the dark curtains to where my dress is hanging, long train looped up elegantly. My friend Kristine made it, fitting the silk to my body with her mouth full of pins while Eve played between us on the floor of her studio. I carried it all the way from New Zealand like a saintly relic. I lean against the doors, fogging the glass with shallow breaths, until Nathalie pushes me out of the way, gently, laughing, with a key in her hand that looks like it opens a dungeon, it's so big and ancient.

Edel and Ruth and Rebecca slip into the little room as I'm getting ready. We laugh and hug and take photos. Sarah sets up a bubble machine for Eve, the translucent bubbles land on my hair as I'm doing my make-up. At the last minute, Edel runs to get some bougainvillea for a bouquet.

'I've never done this before,' says Rebecca. 'Me either,' says Ruth, and we all laugh, maybe for longer than necessary. Nathalie slips her head in the door, and says we're ready. And then we line up, Ruth at the edge, Edel beside her, then me and Rebecca. A pink dress, a bronze satin dress, an ivory dress and a black one. There's a string quartet directly outside our little room, local music students from Perpignan our French friends have organised. When we hear the first notes of Pachelbel's Canon, we link arms and step outside together. We never even thought to practise, but we walk in step somehow, up the aisle to where John is waiting in a blue suit under a green tree for me.

'A bridesmaid in black? I've never seen that,' Mammy sniffs later that night. 'She was lovely though.' Hurriedly. 'They all were, in fairness. But you should have got them matching dresses.'

'They weren't bridesmaids.'

'Of course they were bridesmaids, Noelle, what else were they?'

'My friends, Mammy.'

All my friends who'd come over from New Zealand have heard so many stories about Mammy, they think they'll be getting someone from a Marian Keyes novel. She dismisses them all summarily. I watch from a distance as they rush up to her, full of smiles and excitement, only for her to talk to them briefly, lips in a rictus, and move on quickly. She finds a chair next to Robert and my sister, and says very little except to complain that the French beer is piss water. All the photos I have show her talking behind her hand to Robert, or squinting malevolently, like in a shoplifter mugshot.

'And you didn't even thank me in your speech,' she rings to complain the next morning. 'That was terrible.'

I laugh, with surprise mostly, and also relief she is on her way home, finally.

'Tell John I'm sorry about his fags, the shop was closed. I'll get them for him next time.'

'Don't worry,' I say.

She pulled him off the dancefloor the night before, just after the band started. She knew he had a carton. 'You'd never do me a favour, boy? I'll sort you out tomorrow?'

'Now, Mam?' I looked at her foolishly. We'd just had our first dance when someone said she needed us urgently.

'Yes Noelle, now. He can go. I don't have any.'

John looked at me, face flushed, chest rising and falling.

'I thought you were sick or something!'

'No, I need a cigarette. Go on, I'll get them for you in the Duty Free tomorrow.'

Across the courtyard, our friends were shouting for us. John said, 'Tell them I'll be over in a second.'

'You're very good,' said Mammy, like he had a choice in the matter.

Twenty-four

I'm the first one awake, the cottage is quiet. I'm cold, there's a fuzz of frost on the window. I kicked the blankets off again. I have to stop falling asleep with the electric blanket on. It's so seductive, crawling under the warm covers, but my mouth is dry and horrible-tasting in the morning. I'm only putting on the blanket because I've been sleeping in here on my own, in the children's room of the cottage our friend Helen has lent us. John would never let me. 'If you're cold, put on a jersey,' he sighs every winter, thinking of the electricity bills as I try to mount the heater.

And it's even colder now, since we moved. I never imagined living in the country, but we were sick of feeling like failures for not being able to buy a house in Auckland. We were the only people at the auction for our place in Featherston. They opened a bottle of champagne when we signed, under the big oak tree in the garden. I got the dregs of my takeaway cup of Earl Grey out of the car to do cheers with. The real estate agents clocked it, but they didn't say anything.

Our house has a long veranda, plum and cherry trees, and a chicken coop done up to look like a child's playhouse. There's even a battered rooster weathervane on the gable. 'Look at you, living the middle-class dream,' John says, when we sit around the kitchen table in the evenings, eating French cheese and seedy crackers, me pretending I understand what he's saying when he pores over the plans for the kitchen and bathroom renovations. I get out of the narrow single bed, find my slippers, shuffle out into the hall quietly. John and Eve are in the other bedroom, I don't want to wake them.

I check my phone again, nothing from my sister since 4 o'clock this morning. Mammy's gone to the doctor finally and everything's happening quickly. Sarah said they drugged her for the bronchoscopy, she was freaking out about having a tube down her gullet. Flash of her, the pint in front of her, stubbornly refusing to lower it quickly. 'I can't girl, I've a bird's swallow' – one finger at her throat, infuriatingly. In the photos this morning, wrapped in a pink dressing gown, she looked completely out of it. She was giving the thumbs-up, sitting in the wheelchair, trying to smile, looking posed like the corpse in *Weekend At Bernie's*. She still had her clumpy black sandals on her, with the hospital gown gaping open. She's lost so much weight, none of her clothes fit her.

The kettle boils. I take it outside with the corn bucket, out the front door and down into the middle of the lawn. The mud squelches beneath my gumboots and I take a big gulp of cold air. I pour the water into the stone bird bath that sits in front of the dovecote, melting the thin crust of ice, like Helen showed me.

The day we moved in, very soon after Helen left for the airport, there was a terrible racket at the bottom of the garden, a violent shaking of tree branches, down near the chicken coop. Behind the bushes, on a carpet of pine needles and leaf litter, one of the doves was lying, its snowy white breast marked with two drops of scarlet. 'Must be a hawk,' John said, looking up through the branches above us. He picked up the dead dove, its broken neck lolling, took it away so Eve wouldn't see it. She was banging away on the chickens' water bowl with a stick, oblivious. He took the dead bird to the boundary fence and put it over, laying it on the grass gently.

Back inside the kitchen, washing our hands, I saw a car pull up next to the fence. A woman got out, picked up the dead dove, and drove off with it. God knows what she was doing. About ten minutes later, I went down to top up the hens' water and the air was full of a scream so full of bitterness and rage, I couldn't imagine it wasn't human. But when I looked over to the fence, there was a massive hawk sitting there, bigger than Eve. Its feathers were brown, with a greenish tint that looked unwholesome. Its claws were twisted and yellow, and its beak was open so wide I could see the red of its gullet. It screamed and screamed at me, robbed of its dinner, full of fury. I stood frozen for a couple of seconds, then picked up a sharp stone and threw it over. The hawk rose into the air, still screaming, a long black shadow flying over me. I knew that Eve was safe inside playing, but I ran in to check on her anyway, and locked the door behind me.

Later that night Mammy rings to say she's had an X-ray. She wasn't even going to do that much, only Sarah made her. My sister is sick of her groaning and crying about the backache, refusing to get it checked, saying sanctimoniously, 'I know my own-know.'

'It's clear!' Shouting down the phone at me. 'All clear anyway, he just told me there, thanks be to God and His Blessed Mother.' Her jubilation is touching, after the stoic fatalism earlier. 'He was only a young fella, the radiographer. Check it again, I told him. But nah, 'tis clear all right.' She's talking fast in her excitement, the words tumbling over one another. 'I had to sit outside in that waiting room for an hour. I was frozen. And then he sticks his head out the door and says, "Go on away, you're grand missus"'.

'That doesn't sound very professional,' I say, one eye on the telly. I'm watching *Catastrophe*, the last season, with Carrie Fisher as Rob's mother.

'Ah, he was nice, and look the main thing is the lungs were clear,' she says. 'I'm sure there's something wrong still though. That pain in my back is terrible. Maybe it's osteoporosis, like Han had.'

'Sure get it checked.' On screen, Rob is drinking again, secretly.

'Oh yeah, sure her bones were like glass, my poor mother.'

'Well go away you so, with your spotless lungs. Not that you deserve it!'

'What do you mean Noelle? How dare you!'

'Sure you had a fag in your hand since the first day of secondary school.' I don't know why I went down this road, why I thought I had to be funny.

'Ah go 'way, I was 16 when I started, how dare you?' she says piously. ''Tis clear anyway, thank God. I've to go away now, get my messages. I'm all up in the air with all this. Such disruption.'

'Good night Ma, that's great news,' turning back to the telly.

They aren't clear though. One of them isn't, anyway. There's a text from John Paul when I wake up the next morning: Mass on Mammy's left lung. Large. The radiographer fucked up. I'm sorry.

'I told him not to send you that, in the middle of the night in New Zealand.' Sarah is fuming.

'It doesn't matter. I was awake anyway. How is she?'

'I don't know, she's out somewhere. She's not talking.'

I ring her phone several times. No answer.

They're all furious about the X-ray being misread by the radiographer. It was only her GP ringing to query, alarmed by the weight loss and pain, that made them recheck it. There's talk of suing, now that John Paul is a lawyer. In the end, all that happens is that she's referred for a bronchoscopy.

I shake the food on the platform at the front of the dovecote. Soft, feathery rustles from inside. They don't come out until I'm gone, unless they're really hungry. Eve and I have been hoping to catch them in the bird bath – but she's often at daycare by then, they wait until the sun's out usually. I put on a pot of porridge, stir it steadily. Outside the kitchen window, the low yellow sun is creeping higher. Once Eve's up, we'll go and feed the chickens. She starts shouting from the back steps, before we've even scooped the feed out. Chick-chick-chick, banging the scrap bucket. She strides out to them, a medieval lord distributing largesse to the masses. They step delicately out on their little dinosaur feet to meet her, cluster around and she empties the bucket, covering their heads in cooked pasta and toast crusts.

Sarah says the specialist should know more in a day or two. After Eve goes to daycare, I go for a run around Featherston. Behind the houses with smoke curling from tin chimneys, the green hills rise into the blue sky. I turn up the same cul de sac I run through every morning, wave at the horses in the paddock.

I'm listening to Sinéad O'Connor's first album, enjoying screaming along with her. Back at the cottage, the hens have invaded the veranda. I step past the lavender one and take off my trainers. Sarah texts: Mammy said she's not going back to the specialist.

Twenty-five

The buggy is a piece of shit. Some friend of Sarah's lent it to her. I've been waiting to be sufficiently un-jetlagged to deal with it, but that day doesn't seem to be coming. I'll go mad if we don't get out of the house. Eve kept me awake all last night, tossing and turning, clawing with her mouth and her fingers, from one nipple to another. We should have stopped breastfeeding months ago, I've just been too tired to wean her properly. And she's teething now too, I felt the big molar, breaking ground through the tender flesh of her gum this morning. She's inside in the front room watching *Madagascar*. She'll be square-eyed before we get out of this country.

I google a YouTube tutorial for putting up this brand of buggy. It's supposed to spring up when you push a lever on one of the back wheels, but this one isn't doing it. I rewind the video to see what I'm missing. The presenter is enumerating the features with what looks like genuine excitement. He's an American man with some kids in the background, very clean looking, full of joy and wonder. Religious, I bet you. I kick my foot on the back wheel savagely. The buggy springs open. The seat is dirty. Only chocolate, hopefully. The man on the video has moved onto describing extra features – some kind of hood attachment you buy separately. There's something quite soothing about him, I almost sit down and keep watching. But I have to get out of here, Eve will go mental.

I look at the pile of blue plastic packages on the kitchen table. Jaffa Cakes. Fucking Jaffa cakes. Individually wrapped four-packs, dozens of them. I don't even like them, really. She keeps sending Daddy down here with his arms full of them. I stuff two blue packets in my handbag, they might be handy later. Eve is on the sofa, fully absorbed in what the big lion is doing. 'Come on boo, we're going on an adventure,' I say brightly, ignoring the howls of outrage that come with extinguishing the telly. I'm afraid she's going to break the ropey buggy, but I get her in it and close the stupid safety lock over her little round belly.

It's going to rain – it always rains. I look around and can't find an umbrella. Fuck it, we have coats. I have to get out of this house before I start screaming. This kitchen is too narrow. People raised whole families in these little cottages. I feel dizzy, imagining a mother and a father and children in double digits.

I push my cap down low over my face and pull open the old front door. Directly in our path is a little grey lump of wet toilet paper, from the overflow pipe coming down the wall from the next door neighbours. I lift up the buggy clear of it, straining under the weight of Eve. Flash of Mammy doing the same on North Main Street once. There was a plastic cover on the outside, thin and draughty, slick with rain. Maybe it was Sarah in there, or Robert even? Eve twists and squirms, getting ready to complain. I take out a packet of Jaffa Cakes, tear it open, shove one at her. One of the front wheels of the buggy is loose, it loses traction, whirring crazily.

At the end of the lane, we turn right, and walk up parallel to the stone Cathedral and past The Tower, where I got into trouble once. We were in the Lounge, me and Mammy. There was a new baby, in a pram, a navy blue Silver Cross. It was the size of a car to me, I must have been quite small. Someone pushed back the hood. I looked down at the tiny red-faced thing on the yellow blanket: 'Oooh, it looks like E.T.!' I said. Mammy pulled me away quickly. I said I didn't know why she was giving out to me, I had to say something, and anyway it did look like E.T., and she burst out laughing then and said 'They'd hang you, wouldn't they?' to Carmel.

The buggy stalls, the front wheels doing us no favours. There's little piles of dogshit everywhere. Eve's straps are twisted, I crane around to fix them. Her face is streaked with chocolate too. I dig in the bag for a wet wipe quickly, I don't want anyone to see her like this. Leaning down to scrub her face, my nose fills with the hot stink of dogshit. A smear of brown rolls in and out of view on the back wheel, laying a reeking track on the footpath. Thin, electric currents of rage zip through me. This fucking city.

At the top of Shandon Street, we stand at the crossing and press the button. Big double-decker buses fly down fast towards the Cathedral. John Paul always gets the bus when he comes home from England. Sits upstairs where he can see the whole city. I remember suddenly, when there was smoking on buses. Sitting right up the front of the top deck with Mammy, next to the big metal ashtray that sat on the ground by the window, its black maw open wide for butts and wads of pink chewing gum. You got your tickets on yellow pieces of paper. She always let me hold the money.

All the old shops are gone. The little jewellery shop where we got our Holy Communion crosses, and Mammy got our ribbons cut off a big roll of fabric trims, green for Patrick's Day and red for Christmas. 'The stupid bitch,' she said, when the old woman pierced one of my ears higher than the other, but she never complained. I think the old woman knew her mother. The bakery along from it, that used to have long golden custard creams with dollops of yellow icing in the window, is a hair-braiding place now. The video shop must be someone's flat, a grimy net curtain in front of a streaky picture window. The Old Reliable is still trading, with the two Scottie dogs in the front window, the odd drinker emerging out of the doorway into the dazzle of daylight for a few moments. There's an ugly long crack in the glass in the front window of Sullivan's, where I used to get my Beanos and Buntys. We cross the road, and walk down past the chipper. There's a guy standing beside it in the middle of the footpath, drinking a can of cider, swaying slightly, as if in time to secret music.

I stand outside the Centra. I'm contemplating getting a coffee, even though I know it will be horrible. Just that action of getting a cup, filling it up from the machine, might restore a sense of autonomy. But it will be too hard to hold it and steer the buggy. I get a packet of crisps instead, Eve likes them, and a banana, the only thing that looks vaguely healthy. She hasn't eaten a vegetable or a piece of fruit since we got here. There's a shelf of iced doughnuts by the counter, beige rings puddled in pink icing. I consider them. For the last few days I've been gorging on sugar. We cross the road in front of Shandon. There mustn't be any tourists today, the bells are quiet. I don't even think of The Chimes until we've gone past it. It's boarded up, the name above the windows only faintly visible.

We go to the little park on the right-hand side of Shandon, a graveyard, from the 1700s and full of Quakers with names like

Belinda and Horace. They ran a soup kitchen and there was an almshouse around here too, which is what it was called when kind Protestants gave starving Catholics charity. The grass is long and green between the fallen tombstones. I find us a bench, take Eve out of the buggy, lay the opened packet of crisps in a salty pile between us. I offer her a bit of banana, she won't touch it. I lean forward, take a selfie with the golden fish weathervane of Shandon behind us. I check it's a good one, and post it. Lots of likes immediately, from people still awake in New Zealand. They post saying How cute is Eve and Looks like a great trip and I feel validated, and also like a fraud immediately.

I help Eve down off the bench, she's getting restless. She takes off across the grass and I run ahead of her, checking for bits of broken glass and more dogshit. A couple walk into the park and I'm on alert, I can't be dealing with using addicts this close to my daughter. But then I clock their nice jackets and see that they're tourists. There's a youth hostel across the road. Spanish from the sound of them. They wave shyly. I wave back. I'm so tired. Tired of watching out for everything constantly. I didn't realise how hard this would be. Sarah's at work every day, John's asleep now. I check the phone again, the likes are tapering off on Instagram, I'm lonely. Three more hours until my sister finishes work. I might roast her some vegetables. I feel in my pocket absently for a Jaffa cake and unwrap it before I know what I'm doing. My mouth fills with the sharp sweet taste of dark chocolate and artificial orange.

Mammy's sitting on the sofa, as usual, up at her end, next to the marble fireplace. 'Sit that child down, she'll hop her head off the sofa!' waving her arms in Eve's direction. 'Come on Noelle, now, I'm not able.'

She hasn't even said hello to me. I stalk into the kitchen, grab a packet of Tayto off the kitchen table. 'She's grand, she'll eat these and sit where she is, don't worry about her.'

She's wearing the same clothes she was wearing when we got here a week ago. Her thinness has moved from tiny to uncomfortable. Her face is a map of lines and circles, the bags under her eyes are huge and purple. I register all of this with irritation mostly. Why isn't she trying, when we've come all this way to be with her? 'Ye were down in the park, were ye?' she says eventually. But she doesn't care, really. I can tell by her expression. For the first time in my life, Mammy is not interested in where I've been and what I'm doing. I'm not her focus. It's a new sensation. A weird one.

She's been conspicuous by her absence. Well that's not true, she's not absent, she's either at home or in town, but either way, she's not interested in entertaining us. There was faint talk, when we arrived first, of going to the Wildlife Park or the Donkey Sanctuary, but that isn't happening. 'Take me down to Shandon Street at 12 o'clock, will you?' she shouts in to Daddy, who's sitting at the table. 'I've to get my meat for tomorrow.'

'Meat, right,' Sarah says later. 'Into The Vicarstown, that's where she's going.' The Vicarstown is one of the new bars on her rotation. A proper, young person's bar. I have friends who drink there, but it's quiet in the daytime.

'What's she doing in there?'

'What do you think, Noelle?'

'I can't believe we came all the way from New Zealand, and she doesn't even want to spend time with us. With Eve, even?'

'Ah what did you expect, Noelle? That she'd turn into Granny, and want to drink tea with ye?'

When I told Mammy we were coming, all she said was, 'Well I hope you're not coming on MY account, are ye?' I should have said, Yes we are. You have terminal cancer and I'm bringing your grandchild to see you. It's important. But I just made a bad joke about coming to see the sights, and laughed awkwardly.

After I booked our flights, Mammy rang and screamed at me. 'There's no way in the world Sarah is coming up to Dublin. Do you hear me?' I was in bed, reading Eve a story. I felt my stomach get cold and sick when I heard her voice, drunker than I'd heard her in ages, and furious.

'She's not driving that Dublin road for ye, stop making a fool out of her! Why can't ye fly into Cork anyway, whatever you're doing! You get the fucking train down now, and leave your sister alone, do you hear me? Stop acting the maggot.' She ranted on, Eve knitting her brows at the shouts coming out of the phone.

I texted Sarah: We'll get the train down, I'm not fucking drawing her on me. Don't worry, she replied. Leave her off, I'll come and get ye.

Last week, we went away together, Sarah and me, not once but twice, two hotels in Cork and Kerry. A thanks for all the lifts and for putting us up in her house. We took Eve swimming in fancy hotel pools, ate room service. We called it Sarahpalooza.

'Where are ye now?' Mammy said, agog, when Sarah rang her. 'Parknasilla,' said Sarah, grinning, looking out over the water. We were doing the fairy trail with Eve, looking on tree trunks for the tiny coloured boxes.

'Go 'way out of that, the two of ye are gone out of ye're knowledge. Sure that's five stars isn't it?'

Robert texts later: Do you think you're Bono? I send him photos of the breakfast buffet, the little individual glass bottles of yoghurt, the toaster piled high with different kinds of bread, and the basket of muffins. He texts back: It's unacceptable that I am not part of this. Can't believe you wasted it on Sarah.

•

'She's a grand appetite, anyway, God bless her.' Now Mammy's watching Eve work her way steadily through her morning packet of Tayto. 'Come up on Friday. I'll do her sausages, and jelly and ice cream.'

'Ah you don't have to do that,' I say, thinking of all the nitrates in the sausages, the E numbers in the ice cream, all the sugar. The Taytos are bad enough.

But she's already saying, 'You'll like that, won't you? We'll have a jelly and ice-cream party' in the weird, sing-song voice she used to do for Eve as a baby. 'Would you like that Eve?' 'Come up and have some ice cream with Car-Car?' Her bloody Car-Car, I think, sourly.

'Ice cream,' says Eve equably, pushing a handful of Tayto Snax into herself steadily. I don't know how I'm going to wean her off them.

'Come out here Eve, come here 'til I show you something!' Daddy yells, from out in the back garden. When I bring her out, he has the hose on. He's put a deck out the back, in front of the kitchen window. Where my guinea pig hutch used to be is thronged by a profusion of flowers in pots, hardy perennials mostly, a jungle of colours, purple, orange, red, yellow, very lovely, and faintly institutional looking, somehow. One of my father's contacts works for Cork Corporation, these flowers were originally intended for parks and outside public buildings.

He aims the spray head attachment at a group of pots, soaking them instantly. Eve freezes in wonder, fascinated by the sudden jet of water. 'See, you have to point it at 'em.' He puts the sprayer in one of her fat little hands, wraps the other hand around it, puts his thumb over hers on the trigger. 'Here we go now, little Kiwi!' Eve shrieks as a jet of water shoots out at the flowers. 'Very good, very good.' He turns back to me, grinning. 'I think we have ourselves a little Annie Oakley here, Moll. She likes it, don't she?'

'Ah watch it, John – Jesus, they'll soak the place.' Mammy is beside me, squinting her eyes against the morning sunshine. Eve takes aim again, helped by Daddy. He cheers as she shoots another sparkling arc of water. 'That child will have the head taken off every one of his flowers,' Mammy tuts, but smiling. 'Jesus, she's soaking.' She's twirled the head of the hose around somehow and is standing with her fair curls dripping against a rainbow of wet flowers. The back garden looks bright and cheery, not at all like the concrete desolation I remember from childhood.

'Come on John, will you, I've to get my messages,' Mammy whines, standing beside me. She has her purple anorak on already, and she's holding a reusable bag from Lidl with the parrots on it. She's so agitated and impatient she's shifting from one foot to another.

'Let me out here, let you,' she says when we reach the bridge by the funeral home. He pulls out of the flow of traffic for a second, and she hops down from the jeep, so skinny I think the wind's going to take her.

'Will we go in along to the English market, will we?'

'I don't care.' I know he's trying, but I just don't have it in me. Three weeks was too long, four is lunacy.

'Come on, we'll go in for a look,' says Daddy, nosing the car down Western Road towards town, instead of heading up towards the Northside. He's trying to make this a treat for us, even going so far as to park in a carpark building. 'Robbers,' he says quietly, as the machine spits out the ticket.

Inside, the market is quiet this early in the morning. He stops in front of every stall, offering its contents indiscriminately. 'Do you want a cake? A sausage? Some of them pastries? Go on, let you have one of them.' A full-size birthday cake, by the look of it. 'No, Dad, all I've done is eat since I got here.' Because I can't fucking drink, I think viciously.

We roll Eve around in her buggy. 'This thing is a bit gammy,' he says, once he clocks the front wheel spinning. I glare at him. 'You don't say, Daddy.' We wheel her along past the stalls, making buggy tracks in the sawdust, smelling the familiar iron tang of red meat and the fish stall with its whiff of the ocean. 'Will I get you some of those sure Moll? They're lovely.' He reaches his big fingers towards a gleaming tower of green and purple grapes tumbled on top of each other like jewels in the vegetable shop. 'Do, sure,' I say, more to get him away from me than anything. He goes off and piles them into a small plastic bag that he rubs together to get open, and I think about how open-hearted his love for me is, and how insufficient it feels. He would do anything I asked him, I think as I watch him reach the till, shove a big wide hand into the pocket of his work pants, hand over a note and smile at the woman. She smiles back easily, people always smile at Daddy. Sixty-odd and the hair is thinner, but handsome still, especially when he's grinning. He comes back with the bag of grapes, sits them on top of the buggy. 'Those.' I point at the olive stall, where there are big bunches of West Cork flowers piled on top of the Moroccan crockery. Fuchsia, peach, light pink and purple. Mammy's colours. We got her a bunch from John last time, to say thanks for doing the ironing. 'Those. Will we get a bunch of those, for Mammy?'

'For Civil-Jaws?' He smiles wryly. 'I'm sure she'd love 'em.'

We get a bunch that is mostly pink and purple. Small fragrant wildflowers arranged around an enormous fuchsia-coloured dahlia. It's so big, it's a cartoon of itself, bigger than my head, easily. Before we go, we buy Eve a sausage in a bun with sauce dripping down it. It's delicious. I eat most of it, in the car driving up to Hollymount.

Carol takes the flowers grudgingly. 'Put them down there, I've to take my medicine.' But even she's amazed by the dahlia. 'Is that real?' she says, putting it into the vase with the others. 'You never see them that big.'

'It's from West Cork, Ma. Fairy magic.' I look at her for a moment, holding the giant flower. 'Come on so,' I clap my hands. 'Photo shoot.'

This could go either way, she's lost interest since her diagnosis. She brushes me off at first. 'Ah go 'way Noelle, wait 'til I'm done up some time. I've no make-up on or anything, I'm terrible.' But I just point at the flower and at her hair, move my finger back and forward from one to the other. 'Come on. It's too good not to. The exact same colour.'

'Ah my hair needs doing ages ago.' But she turns from the kitchen sink, bends her elbow obligingly, so the giant flower sits on the side of her head lightly. In the photo, she's not smiling exactly, but her eyes, mostly downcast, show the slightest hint of good humour. Her face is already lined in a way it wasn't the year previously, her hand is thinner and her collarbone is razor sharp where her white top gapes open. I don't notice any of this until months after I take the photo.

'You can put it down now, I'm surprised you don't need two hands to hold it.'

'Amazing, sure, isn't it? What a beautiful flower,' she says, her small pink head fitted neatly beneath it.

Walking past the narrow houses that sit side by side under the bell tower of Shandon, I stop and watch the evening sun catch fire in the laneway alongside me. Mammy used to push me down there, hurrying from one hideyhole to another, or walk me down, alongside my brother, or my sister in the buggy. Out onto Shandon Street to meet Philly and Carmel, or over briefly to the toy shop to buy marbles or pretty scrap paper for us to play with. They used to borrow money from Claire in the toy shop, John Paul told me years later, to see them through to Children's Allowance. The shop had gas bottles in the window, hanging high up above the Barbies.

At the meeting tonight, everyone came up and shook my hand at the end, as well as the speaker's. 'And we want to thank Noelle too, for your lovely contributions, we'll miss you. Have a lovely time in England, and safe back to New Zealand,' said Eileen, before we said the serenity prayer. Eileen is kind, with her soft country accent, and her big hair, and her can of Fanta on the table in front of her. People clapped when she said it and I looked down quickly, so nobody would see the tears in my eyes. I've been coming to this room for years now, twice a week, three times sometimes, whenever I'm back in Ireland. Barrelling in without warning or notice, sharing whenever I'm asked, spilling out how frustrated I feel, how lonely it is, being the only one not drinking, trying to stay out of arguments, trying to avoid recriminations, failing. Meetings are different in Ireland than in New Zealand. Here one person does 'the chair', starts the meeting off by telling their story. Over time, I've come to know everyone's struggles, with family, work, health, money. I know where a lot of them got sober, in treatment centres with saints' names in different parts of the country. They know about my life too, how I got sober in Auckland.

A few years ago, a man who always sits in the same chair, in the left-hand corner, came up to me when I was leaving. I'd shared in the meeting that I was worried about going back to New Zealand. 'These are for you,' he said, putting something in my hand that didn't weigh anything. 'I got them in Vietnam, on my holidays. From the monks. You can pray with them, or just wear them.' The beads are made out of some fragrant wood, smooth beneath my fingers. I think of them now, in a red pouch in my bedroom in Featherston.

Tonight, I sat against the wall in my usual place, on the far side of the room, towards the corner. I closed my eyes and listened. A beautiful young girl said she dreads the long summer evenings, they make her want vodka. I thought about Ruth, and Edel, the nights at the bars with the white walls and high ceilings. This is still a young person's town and always will be. Afterwards, several of the older women circled around the girl. Others came up and shook my hand, said good luck now, and we'll see you again next summer. We laughed, and we hugged and said next time, we'll definitely do a dinner. Everyone wished Mammy well, with such kindness that I wanted to cry with embarrassment and gratitude.

The sun floods the little street. I'm 12 years old again, running home, sprinting from bus stop to bus stop, running my own private 100 metres, across the top of the estates towards Hollymount, smoke from the bonfires hanging in the air. I was ready to leave here for as long as I can remember, ready to go and never look back, ready to renounce everyone. And now here I am, and I've spent the last three weeks pushing my baby around Shandon in a busted buggy, just like my mother. Behind me is the graveyard where I used to play while Mammy was in The Chimes. I cut my leg in there once, on a broken Carling bottle, so deep I could see the pale layer of fat beneath my skin glisten for a second, before it started bleeding. I still have the scar on my knee, a little white sickle. Even if I spend my whole life until I die, on the other side of the planet, as far away as it's possible to get from here, I'm never leaving. Mammy and Daddy, and Hollymount, and John Paul and Sarah and Robert, no matter where I go, they will always be part of me. I stand in the flaming orange light of the evening sun and I'm OK. It's all OK, this is my city.

I text Sarah: Will we get chips and curry? She texts back: Daddy's getting it for us. It's ordered already.

Twenty-six

Up in the bedroom under the eaves, with dusk turning to night proper, I peel Eve off what's left of my breast and lay her down next to John, who is sleeping, crushed with jetlag. In the light from the bedside lamp, her lashes make two perfect fans on her flushed cheeks. I turn off the lamp and leave them, closing the door behind me.

Our in-laws-to-be have put us all up together in this row of holiday cottages just along from their family home. The front door of Sarah's cottage is open. I come through and find them all, John Paul, Sarah and my mother, in the backyard. John Paul and Sarah have a bottle of champagne between them, laughing at Mammy holding court across the table. I feel that small sting I get sometimes, when I see them all together, enjoying themselves without me. Mammy's smiling, raising a cigarette to her mouth. She looks happier than I've seen her all summer, surrounded by her children, the old triumph radiating off her.

She's skinnier than she was in Cork two days ago. Her neck is raw and stringy, like a chicken. But she seems to have grown too, somehow. Puffed out in a way that I know isn't physically possible. It's just the satisfaction she gets from having her children around her, it makes her seem bigger.

'Go and make a cup of tea, Noelle,' she says impatiently.

'Where's the kettle, Sarah?'

'On the counter, Noelle – where else would it be?'

'I'll have one too. Go in next door and get the good tea bags,' Mammy shouts. 'That English tea is rotten.'

I stick my head around the door, look at her quizzically. 'YOU want tea?'

'What, Noelle? She's tired.' Sarah says quickly.

'Yeah, I can't have anything, that wine would sicken me.' Mammy groans again. 'Make a cup of tea, would you.' I make the tea in mugs, put them on a tray with milk in a jug and a packet of chocolate digestives. Out in the dark garden we laugh at John Paul softly.

'Oooh, someone's gonna be a husband tomorrow!' Mammy sings, in the voice that drives us all crazy.

'Are you excited about losing your virginity, John Paul? Is there anything you want to ask me?' I say brightly.

He doesn't even bite, just twirls the lock of hair in front of his forehead, smiles enigmatically. He has a dreamy look on his face, he's either very drunk or contemplating his future.

'Don't be so disgusting, Noelle,' Sarah says automatically. She sips her wine, her eyes dancing. They've finished the first bottle of bubbles, moved onto a second. It still has the Duty Free foam protector around it. Mammy gets me to break a biscuit in half for her, holds it delicately. Her fingers, always long and lovely, are now thin and gnarled.

Mammy keeps saying she must go into bed, but she doesn't go

anywhere. She's probably waiting for me and Sarah to go, so she can have John Paul to herself. Or maybe she's waiting up for Robert, who's flying in later. The night's clear and starry, a taste of the sea in the air. And that indefinable something that lets you know you're not in Ireland, although everything's so similar.

When it comes down to it, I don't know why I don't like England. The chocolate is not as good, but the newspapers are better, the people are fine, mostly, even with the accent. 'It's just strange, you know, different,' I said to John in Bristol. I was trying to explain my dislike, which has gotten worse as I have gotten older. 'It's all the annoying things about Ireland – bad weather, terrible food in cafes, racism – and none of the entertainment.' There's a tamped-down quality to everything that I find frustrating.

But sitting in the garden, hearing the soft noises of what might be a hedgehog, the navy-blue night sky above us, I'm just glad to be in the Northern Hemisphere. Everyone says it's time to go to sleep, but we sit outside for a while longer, John Paul trying to get Mammy to tell the old stories about her cousin. Was she the one who never drank in her life, and then got pissed on brandy and became an alcoholic at the age of 50? Was he the one who secretly recorded everyone with the video camera? We're all laughing, together, not at each other. There's a moment when it feels like we might be normal.

The next morning at the Town Hall, John Paul and his wife sign the register up on a little dais. Mammy makes them hold the position while she paws around in her bag for the disposable camera. Our new in-laws fold around the bride, crying happily after the ceremony. Looking at them, the shame I feel is reflexive. They are kind, not only to us, but to each other. I'm embarrassed by Mammy, not wanting to talk to anyone, and by how we all are – snarling at one another, stressed out of our minds in general.

On the drive there I told her, 'Stop making everything so fucking hard for everyone. Stop being so damn selfish, we're here for a wedding!' When she got into the car she was already shrewish, irritating me so much with her negativity that I almost couldn't do up the straps on Eve's car seat. I sat in the back beside the child, listening to her relentless stream of how stupid these roads were, how exhausted she was, what a hassle everything was, why the fuck did they have to get married in England.

By the time we found a parking space, we were ten minutes late and my whole body was shaking. Ten years I've spent, a whole fucking decade, doing twelve-step meetings, therapy, praying, all for the same outcome: so I could learn to stop taking out my problems on others. And here she is, doing it to all and sundry, as she'd been doing since the day I was born probably. We got out of the car, the sun beating down on us. I never in my life wanted a drink so badly – not one drink, all the drinks, and to hell with everything. What was the point of trying to do anything, except satisfying my own worst impulses? Where does self improvement actually get you? A very big drink was what I needed, or a knife to stab her. John came up close to my ear and squeezed my fingers. 'Don't give her any oxygen.' It was on the tip of my tongue to tell him to go fuck himself, what does he know about my mother. But I just breathed out heavily onto the top of Eve's head and felt the sweat pooling in my armpits.

Before we leave the Town Hall, we take a family photo. We're all mugging for the camera, only there's a few of them pointing at us: Sarah and I are looking in completely different directions to everyone else. John Paul's in the middle in tortoise-shell glasses, looking stunned with happiness, his arms around me on one side and Mammy on the other. Mammy comes up to his armpit, so visibly ill it feels like an intrusion to look at her. Her cheeks have fallen in, the rouge sits on top, an obvious falsehood. The two-piece she's wearing is the palest shade of pink, skin-coloured, so she looks not only emaciated, but naked. She spends the rest of the day hiding from all the people who wanted to talk to her at the reception. I find her, wrapped in a blanket, hiding behind a clump of sea grass, smoking.

'Stop that you,' she hisses, as I point my phone at her. 'Go away, can't you! Leave me in peace, I'm ducking people.'

The car's almost too big to fit down the narrow lane. The driver turns at the bottom and idles outside the last cottage. Sarah ducks out of the open doorway with Mammy's bag in her hand, flings it into the open boot. It's the Betty Boop one from Penneys, the same one she brought to my wedding. It was open in her bedroom earlier. I was going through it before I knew what I was doing. The blouse and jacket she wore for the wedding on top, folded neatly. A card for my brother and his wife in a green paper bag from Blarney Woollen Mills beneath it. Her jewellery in the bright orange pouch from Brown Thomas, the little plastic sandwich bag with her toothbrush and toothpaste, Astral cream and a bottle of Estée Lauder. Loads of different medicines. The pouch with her diabetes reader.

Later, much later, I'll understand a bit better what it must have been like for Mammy, coming over here, sick as she was, dreading the prospect of cancer treatment. To come all the same, all the way to England. Up at six for the coach to Dublin, a full day's travel, to run the gauntlet of well-meaning strangers. Later, I'll cry looking at photos, wonder how I didn't see it written on her body – the matchstick legs, the skinny neck poking out of the collar of the Champion ski jacket. But that's all in the future. On this morning in September in Dorset, I'm just fucking sick of her.

'Come on, Mam.' Sarah must be close to cracking. Mammy let loose on her last night when they came back from The Red Lion, Sarah trying to get her out of the taxi before anyone saw her. I didn't actually hear what she was shouting, just a quick burst of noise, ripping through the still evening and subsiding just as quickly. I knew enough not to walk out onto the lane, and Eve was beside me anyway.

I sprinkle pebbles on the ground for Eve to catch, ignore my mother standing in front of me. I can look right though her, I have so many years of practice.

'Mam!' Sarah barks this time, she's done waiting.

'All right, all right, for fuck's sake,' she mutters, pushing the stinking fag butt into the tin, doing up her white jacket. She bends down slightly, kisses the air over the top of Eve's head and says 'God bless now' solemnly. Eve looks up for a second, then turns back to her pebbles.

John, coming out of our cottage, takes in that she's going to walk straight past him and says diplomatically, 'Bye so, Carol.' She stopped talking to him 48 hours ago. No reason, other than guilt by association.

She turns her back to me then, pre-empting my cold shoulder.

'Goodbye,' I call to her, not wanting to give her the satisfaction of having been the one who didn't say it.

Mammy walks to the other side of the car, past us. Her jeans are so big now, it's almost comical. Even belted, they're hanging off her. I notice her fly is completely open. Think about telling her. Decide not to. Fuck it, she'll only shout at me anyway. She slams the car door. I see Sarah turning irritably to face her. Telling her to put her seatbelt on.

The driver releases the handbrake, the car moves forward.

Twenty-seven

She says she's going home, when I go in to see her. She got some fool doctor to sign her out – she was calling a taxi when I caught her. She sat on her bed with her toilet bag in her hands, furious and snarling like a trapped ferret, while I stood in the hallway, pleading with the nurse in a whisper. She'd told the doctor on duty there was a home-care package all set up, that she'd met with the palliative care nurse, and was booked in for future meetings. All lies. But the doctor didn't check anything she told her, and with nothing acutely wrong with her, there is now no real reason to keep her in here. She was admitted two weeks ago on the brink of a diabetic coma, but her bloods are relatively stable now, and she doesn't even need the nebuliser. She is not sick per se, only dying. And everyone says, if she won't go to hospice, home is the best option. A nurse could come and top up her morphine, check her bloods. She could sit and smoke on her own sofa, preparing to meet her maker. Except there's a three-week wait and only part-time nursing help available. Mammy's sofa is covered in dog hair, and about 25 years of crap and detritus. In recent years, she's become a hoarder. Bags and bags of clothes from the charity shop, books, toys for Eve, broken china. She started stockpiling sweets after she was diagnosed with diabetes. I go up there, throw out a bin bag full of chocolates, fizzy drinks, a whole Christmas cake wrapped up in tinfoil. Returning her to Hollymount is untenable, not only because it's a junkyard, but also because my father is terrified. His face goes white when she talks about coming home – he's afraid of finding her dead in the night, or worse, having to give her some medicine and inadvertently killing her. If I could talk about such things, I would explain to him that he's being triggered by the trauma of what happened to his mother, but we don't talk about that, so instead I make the nurse promise my mother won't be discharged that night, and text Dr Byrne.

He gets us into his office – me, Daddy, John Paul, Sarah, all crouched around a cluttered white table. Robert's at work maybe, nobody is certain.

My father looks like a gorilla squashed in a phonebox, jammed in between my sister and my brother. Byrne offers his hand to him, says how sorry he is that they haven't spoken before now. 'I asked her if I could meet with ye, wouldn't she bring her husband in, at least,' he'd said on the phone, last week, when I was still in New Zealand. 'No, she said, oh no, they wouldn't be able for it.' I'd nearly screamed then. At the selfishness of it, the absolute fucking full-stop of her refusal to do anything to make it easier for anyone.

Byrne sits close to us, smelling of soap, faintly. 'She's a lovely person, Caroline, a real lady. She brought us all in boxes of chocolates.' Well yes, I think, she has plenty. 'She's a lovely woman, but she wouldn't let me talk to any of ye.'

We shake our heads in unison around the table. 'That's what she's like sure,' my Dad sighs, big hairy paws on the table. Banana hands, John Paul calls him. His thumb pads have big calluses, from unblocking u-bends, pushing pipes into joinery.

Byrne says, you must have questions. We ask about morphine, hypoglycaemia, insulin, and the condition she was admitted with, diabetic ketoacidosis. There is, he tells us, a complex web of different reactions and chemical processes that will eventually kill our mother. 'Her body is in the process of shutting down. How long that takes is up to every individual. It is happening, though, and it will continue.'

But she nearly got out last night, she keeps trying to get home! Sarah looks like she's about to start crying. 'Yes, I'm sorry. But the hospital really isn't the right place for her. Not at this stage. Tell me, does she know she's dying?'

We look at each other blankly. I ask him 'Haven't you told her?' John Paul tells me later, that is not a conversation doctors ever have unless patients ask directly.

'Er, that might be something for you all to think about.' Sarah says she'll do it. I can't imagine anything worse than trying to introduce Mammy to her own mortality. The last time I rang her from New Zealand, she was adamant: 'I'll be grand, girl, I've great faith altogether.'

Byrne talks up Marymount again. Apparently there's a drinks trolley. But she prefers drinking at home, in private. You can smoke there too, which you would think would be a deal breaker. Forty a day since she was about 14. But she remains unmoveable.

'There's 22 people waiting on this bed down in A&E, Carol,' Sarah heard him say to her earlier. He was on his actual knees, she said, down on the ground looking up at Mammy.

'Are there?' she says, looking down at him. 'Then why don't you just let me go home and give it to one of them?'

Byrne lets us out, one after the other, dazed and quiet into the corridor, where we stand in front of a portrait of a dour-faced Sister of Mercy.

'I'll go 'way, get some food, let ye go on up to her.' John Paul rakes his hand through his hair, pushes the lift button. Sarah can barely wait for the doors to shut on him. 'Where do you think he's going?' 'The Chateau, surely. For a "bowl of soup".' I put finger quotes around it. Bowl of soup my hole, he's going drinking. I don't begrudge him.

Up in the ward, Mammy is in a foul humour. She berates Sarah for getting the wrong tissues, the ones she spent yesterday driving all over the city for. 'And you!' glaring over at me with her too-big, opium-bright eyes narrowed. 'Look at you, messing up everything. You're so bloody awkward!' All my life she's called me clumsy. In fairness, I'm sitting on the edge of her bed, and I've upset the covers. There's a magazine sliding off the edge of the blanket as well – she snatches at it, the drips and cords waving like garlands. 'Just pick it up! Leave me alone, you're so bloody useless, you are!'

'Mam, stop, Noelle came all the way from New Zealand.'

'She didn't fucking walk it, Sarah.' Mammy lies back on her pillows, 'Go home now let ye, ye are exhausting me.'

I go downstairs, seething. She's always the same. Taking no advantage whatsoever of the chance to make her peace with people. Intent on this 'going home' madness. Clearly this is the final destination. She's a nurse, for Christ's sake, how can she not see this? But it's been the same for the last ten months, ever since her initial diagnosis. Not that she would even go to the doctor for ages, even though we begged her. 'No, girl, no. I'll go in my own time. That's my own business.' Hacking down the phone to me, moaning in pain some evenings. 'Please, just go get it checked.' I tried to be casual, matter-of-fact, chatty, cycling through all the different registers, trying to convince her. I'd sit with my hands shaking afterwards, wondering why I was getting so upset, then realising what those conversations reminded me of: all the times when I was younger, when I'd ask her, plead with her, try to reason with her, somehow get her to stop drinking.

'I'm so sorry – I just wish things were different, I will get her a private room ASAP,' Byrne texts later. I go to bed that night thinking of all the deathbed scenes I've watched or read between mothers and daughters, the tender benedictions, passing on of wisdom. Laughable, all of them. I just want to go home, and have it all be over. I never even wanted to see her before she died; we have nothing to say to one another.

On the sky bridge between the wards and the main part of the hospital, there's a mother and her daughter. Big women, Travellers from the up-and-down sound of them. The girl has beautiful thick dark hair and is eating a pink-and-white ice cream coated with little bits of pink biscuit. A Brunch, it's called – when I was small, I used to love them. Her make-up is a thick clown mask, like all the young girls wear here: red-brown foundation, pink lips, blow-up-doll colour, black-browed eyes with spider lashes. They sit on the windowsill, an aerosol can of Dove deodorant between them. The daughter asks the Mam for 20 Euro. Her pyjama pants have planets on them, the top says Cosmic Girl in glitter.

The next morning it's just me and Mammy. My cases are packed back at Sarah's.

'Go 'way you, I'm trying to duck you,' she shouted in her thin little voice, warding me off when she saw me.

She's always hated goodbyes. Every time I'm leaving to go back to New Zealand, she stands in the hallway, dousing me from the filthy milk bottle full of Holy Water, saying 'You're only going on your holidays, you'll be back next week' over and over.

Sitting on the bed beside her, my stomach drops away and I'm overcome by nerves suddenly, like it's my first time kissing a boy or something. Her lunch tray is already on the rolling table next to the bed, a metal bowl half-filled with grey, and little pieces of carrot. 'It's the same every day, for God's sake,' she says – like she even tastes it. She's trying to pretend to the nurses that she's eating, John Paul caught her the other night with a sandwich under her pillow.

She's looking into her locker, the jumble of tissues and lotion, Mass cards and secret things she's hoarded: those biscuits she collects up for me, and mandarin oranges. Her shoulder blades stand out like two wings on her back, and I'm crying suddenly. She turns around and I see that she is too, big fat tears sliding down her ravaged cheeks effortlessly.

'Close that will you, don't let them see,' she cries out, pointing with clawed fingers towards the blue paper curtains on either side of us. They open like fans when I pull them, and then we are alone together in the underwater light. I hold her, very gently so as not to shatter the tiny, sharp bones beneath me.

'Mamma.' I started calling her that a few years ago. An affectation, but it's my name for her. I kiss her small head, the pink tufts of hair already falling out of it.

'You'll come back again, on another visit,' she says, not looking at me. I push myself alongside her on the edge of the bed, my arm still around her. 'You'll come back again, and we'll go to Kerry.'

'Which part? Not a boring part, not that place with the windmill.'

'Blennerville,' she sighs. 'Ah, I don't mind. Any of it. We'll make our own fun.'

'OK so, we'll go to Kerry.' There's so much salt in my eyes, my vision is blurry. Through the gap in the curtains I can see the woman in the bed across from us, sitting in front of her own bowl of soup, not moving. 'OK, so. Kerry. We'll go.' I sniff loudly, wipe my nose on my jumper. She waves her free hand in my direction, the one I'm not holding. The clear plastic drip holders around her wrist rattle against each other like a bracelet.

'You go away now, and when you go, just get up and go, don't be making me cry and upsetting me.'

This is the last time I will see my mother. I try to be very clear about this in my head, so I won't forget anything. I can't believe I am really going, but my ticket to the airport coach is on my phone, downloaded. How can I go? She's still alive, it's not finished. I can't go, but I miss my daughter. I'm frightened of not being allowed back in with this virus spreading.

I take her in my arms again, her little pink skull against my shoulder, her plush dressing gown in the ice-cream colours, her face so changed and scary. The big black bruise blooms in the crook of the arm she puts around me. I reach both arms around her and they overlap behind her back there's so little of her. I love you I love you I love you, my heart beats it out strong and true and all those things I said and did, the times I threw her vodka down the sink and slapped her face and bit her and said I hate you, they are all with us too. You came out of me, she used to scream, you came out of me, you did, as I tore the thin freckled skin of her forearms, gouged out tracks in her with my nails when I was 12, 13, full of the strength of hating her. I would get down on my knees now and climb back up inside her. I am yours, the first one you kept, the one you had at Christmas, I am yours, you bless me each time I walk out of your hallway. I am yours. I love you, you are in me, you are inside me. I hit you I beat you I shook you. I am sorry. I love you Mammy. I knew you.

I kiss her temples again and I am full of wonder. I thought I knew why I came over here and now I know that I didn't know anything. Lips to her waxy skin, the stink of hospital chemicals in my nostrils mixed with the first smell of my life, the sweet, wolf-den smell of my mother. I take a deep breath, breathe her out again gently. To my utter surprise, I know what to do now. I know what to say and what to do and how to let these last few moments play out between us. Everything is bigger than us, and only us at the same time, and there's that feeling again, of having been allowed, for a moment, to see into a powerful mystery.

'I love you, you are amazing.' She doesn't say anything, I don't need her to.

'And Dr Byrne thinks you're amazing.' I think he does, anyway. I know she'll like me saying it.

'Does he? When were you onto him?' Her eyes bright at the thought of the two of us talking about her.

'I rang him yesterday. He's never met anyone like you.'

'Ah go 'way.' Almost bashful. She's a nurse, still, invested in that hospital hierarchy.

Another kiss on the brow, I can feel the bone of the eye sockets beneath my lips.

I'm relaxed now. I keep my arms around her. Her chart's on the table, next to the soup bowl. I read it upside down. Weight on admission: 35kg. We take selfies. Later, when I look at them on the bus to the airport, my eyes in the photos are red and swollen. She looks like she's dead already. I show her some shots of Eve, in West Cork from last summer.

'She looks nice, she's dressed nice there.'

'You bought her those leggings.' She doesn't remember.

Don't drink, no matter what. An American woman who comes to our AA meeting in Featherston says the same thing every Thursday.

One more kiss on the top of her head. I pull back the paper curtain. 'Bye Mamma. I love you.'

She won't look over, won't do the last goodbye. 'Go on away now girl, go on, don't be upsetting me.'

Twenty-eight

The bird comes in on the day she dies and comes every day for a week after. I know she's gone as soon as it flies in the door. Pīwakawaka are festive birds, the fan of the tail makes them look like little Christmas ornaments. This one fills the house with a brave and piercing 'cheep cheep' as it swings back and forth on the long cord of the lightbulb, like a tiny Tarzan.

I am in Eve's bedroom, picking toys up off the floor, when the phone starts humming. I straighten up with two plastic blocks in my hand, one red, one orange. My sister is crying. I look out across the hall, through the kitchen windows, and everything is golden: the evening sun on the yellow stalks of tall grass in the overgrown vegetable patch, the yellow paint on the dining room walls, the fabric of my apron. Everything burnished and bright and godly.

'She's gone now. She just went there.' Sarah, soft and resigned, far from inconsolable.

'And it's a beautiful, sunny evening in New Zealand,' I say, like a fucking sports announcer.

I pick up a piece of Lego, put it in the box with the others.

'Well Moll, she's gone. Sarah was with her.' My Dad next, tired-sounding, telling the end of a story. I look down and stare at the floor in the Mercy, pale-coloured linoleum with a faint grey marbling. A smell of bleach and disinfectant mixed with boiled vegetables, something soft and bloody beneath it. Outside, it will be cold still, and pitch dark. February is over, but in Cork spring will be taking its time, as usual.

'She's gone.' Robert. His voice is childishly nasal, in my head he's still the baby.

'I know. I'm sorry Robert,' I say, formally. We never talk on the phone usually.

'I'm sorry I'm not there.'

'Don't be. It'll be terrible.'

He knows I'm glad to be missing it. Soup and salad sandwiches in some barn of a pub in Blarney. Ancient neighbours from Chapel Hill sympathising. And the drinking. He'll be fine, with a few in him.

'What time is it there?' None of my family ever know the time in New Zealand when they ring me.

'It's 6 o'clock. Nearly dinnertime.'

He perks up. 'What are ye having?'

'Fish cakes.'

'Disgusting.'

John Paul doesn't come on the phone. Later, I get a text that says 'Finis'. He'll go back to London now, finally.

I walk down to my own dim room; the gold velvet curtains are still closed from the night before. I stand in front of the little shrine on top of a chest of drawers. There's jasmine in the glass milk jug, a couple of photos, the expensive candle from Duty

Free in Dublin that I bought to use up my euros. The little flame flickers behind the blue glass, the room is full of the sweetness of the wild flowers mixed with the clean, sharp scent of bergamot. She looks back at me: a grandmother, eyes bright, face too thin already, posing in the kitchen with her pink dahlia last summer. She's a teenager in a short red dress in the other photo, leaning against an old water pump in Kerry, her hands full of daffodils – or maybe they are yellow irises, the photo is 50 years old and a bit fuzzy. A metal bucket rests against the curve of her knee, filling up with water. Pale oval face, long white arms and legs, dark hair blowing. In blue pen, in her careful, childish handwriting on the paper mount of the photo: Caroline Mary, Station Road, Glenbeigh 1970. I drop to my knees. Not thinking, it's an instinct. I pray for her, for me, for everyone. It's still bright on the other side of the curtains.

Twenty-nine

The casket is in front of the altar, in the centre of the aisle, I'm looking straight at it. It's covered with a white cloth and one framed photograph of her wearing my rabbit fur jacket. From where I'm sitting, I can see only the backs of everyone's heads – Daddy, Sarah, Robert and his girlfriend. In the row behind them, Mammy's sister and her brothers. The altar is empty still, the priest hasn't yet materialised. My flowers are on a stand beside the casket, a riot of colours and tall birds of paradise. I can smell the jasmine I picked for her this morning, sweet and heavy in the night air. It's midday in Cork, 2am in New Zealand, and Mammy's funeral is about to begin on the laptop in front of me.

I didn't think it would work. Right up until the moment I clicked on the livestream earlier. I'm here in the dark now, in my pyjamas with a cup of tea, like I'm watching Netflix. But it's the altar of the North Cathedral in front of me, the white marble as smooth and cold as ten days ago, when I last knelt at it. Behind the altar is the big stained-glass window that floods the church with bright blue light in the late morning, so every prayer feels blissful and underwater. The pulpit's where it always is, off to the left. I walked up there and read The Lord is My Shepherd at Nana's funeral. Everything on the screen is pale-coloured except for my flowers – white tiles, white walls, the white cloth covering the coffin. I asked for the flowers to be bright on purpose. Everything else is calm and cold and holy. There's a bit of static on the audio feed in the headphones I'm using – John and Eve have been asleep for hours – and then the first rolling notes of a church organ and what sounds like a pub singalong or football club chorus. The Boys Choir. They sound older. At first they're ragged, but the voices blend together eventually into a solemn hymn, uplifted by the organ. The Mass has begun. She would have loved this. John Paul speaks first: I can't hear him, only watch his familiar silhouette, shoulders slanted, head drooping at the lectern, curly hair dropping onto his forehead. The priest, resplendent in purple, rushes to fix the microphone and I hear the voice of my brother. He sounds matter-of-fact and confidential, a lawyer already. His tribute references Mammy's high jinks with Philly, and finishes with a lengthy quote from *Angels in America*. Most of the crowd present, being unfamiliar with landmark trilogies about the AIDS epidemic, haven't the slightest idea what he's on about, but it's beautiful. The priest says a few words. He calls Mammy by her sister's name at one point, but apart from that, he seems surprisingly familiar with her. She was a very private person, he says, but a very good one. She was private and determined, he says, which is as good an encapsulation as any. There is talk of seasons: times to kill and heal, times to weep and laugh. My brother comes back and reads Ezekiel, then Wilfred

Owen: 'fill these void veins full again with youth' . . . 'my head hangs weighted with snow.' Her bruised arms in the hospital bed, the pink-and-white hat on her head.

Len comes and reads Psalm 23. His voice is strong and deep through the Cathedral.

Yea though I walk through the Valley of Death I will fear no evil.

He moves away, as quick and neat as he was flying through town with me, all through my childhood, the cinema and Burger King every Wednesday. He rang Carol every Saturday to tell her what the weather was like at his house: 'Very fine down here this morning!' 'I know, Len,' she'd say, 'I'm only ten minutes away.' The priest says something about Mammy's perfection. I write this in my notebook, and put WTF next to it. Even a perfect person fails seven times in a day, a quote from the Book of Proverbs. I write this down too, it's encouraging. Auntie Cay's voice shakes when she does her reading. Her fancy black hat wobbles on screen. Two of the aunts on Daddy's side do Prayers of the Faithful in winter boots and bright quilted jackets. Their voices are soft and they read each word carefully. Her brother Pat's prayer rings out effortlessly, he is a Seanachaí, storyteller, he goes to festivals all over the world with it, he's a natural entertainer. 'Grief is its own thing,' he told me before I went back to New Zealand, over cold tea in the place in the Crawford. 'About two years, it'll take, before you're right again. Just let it take you.'

Bob next, her youngest brother, hesitant. He flew 40 hours from Melbourne to get here. More readings, more talking. A Dominus Tecum, and the Ave sung by a lone chorister. Would she like this? She would love it. Except her sister's frilly black hat, like Miss Havisham – Carol would be furious at this blatant attempt to pull focus. Spotlights throw a soft pink light on the wall behind the priest's throne at the back of the altar. I know the colours well from the mornings I spent there.

I push the headphones off for a second, and I'm back in my silent room in Featherston. I put them back on and the choir is singing Hosanna in Excelsis. 'She is fallen asleep in the hope of resurrection,' the priest is saying. She told Dr Byrne that the Lord would save her.

My sister and my father haven't moved throughout the service. Sarah's hair is curled perfectly, my Dad's bald scalp is ringed by a bright white tonsure. There's a prayer for peace, and a thanksgiving for a life well lived. I could query that, but who am I to judge?

My screen gives me a view of the old wooden bench in front of a stand of votive candles in the left-hand corner of the Cathedral. I know without seeing that there's a narrow stained-glass window above it, depicting Christ on the cross in a modernist style, all black lines and angles. That was always the most exciting place when I came here with Granda, the prospect of being allowed to light a candle when Mass was over. The coin, cold in my fingers, slipped into a slot, taking a small white candle from the pile, the wax making my fingers slightly greasy. The best bit then, touching my candle to one already lighting, the flame jumping from one to another. Consciousness of the small heat in my hand, putting it in its metal holder. I say the same prayer now, in the dark of my study. I put the candle beside the photo of Mammy and her dahlia. I'm glad we took that photo, even though she was such a bitch last summer. In the Cathedral, there's a lot of choreography on the altar. Two women use a bottle of hand sanitiser before picking up the vessels full of communion. The lone voice again. How Great Thou Art. Her favourite. I look over at her with her dahlia, half expecting her to say something. My father takes communion for the first time in ages.

After the Eucharist, the audio feed is empty for about 30 seconds. I watch the early afternoon sunlight spread out in a circle on the marble at the edge of the altar. It is spring now, almost.

'The family will now prepare the casket for burial,' the priest says, surprising me.

All the pantomime of this stuff. I watch them come forward, the five of them, range around the coffin, gathering up the fabric on either side of it. My fingers twitch, I want to help them. But it comes off smoothly, underneath it, the deep glow of the wooden casket.

Sarah crying, Daddy's hand on her shoulder. I am still taking notes – here in New Zealand they are all characters in my story.

The women – Sarah, John Paul's wife Juliet, Robert's girlfriend Steff – all stand in a little huddle beside the coffin as the priest intones the final Prayers of Commendation.

The shades have lengthened, the evening has come.

They start rolling the casket down the aisle. Something about safe lodging, holy rest and peace in parting.

The priest's robe glows even brighter as, off-screen, the sun climbs higher.

He swings his incense, the air in my room is thick with the expensive smell of a French candle. They start the last song, a dirge called Bring Her Home. People pour out of their pews, my father, his sisters and brothers, her siblings, masses of people; old friends and neighbours.

As the coffin leaves the screen I am hit by a wave of loneliness. I want them to wheel her back up where I can see her. I watch the screen fill up with an array of faces, figures with hair long and short, grey and coloured, winter coats and scarves wrapped around them. Ruth walks into the frame for a second, in her padded coat she looks about twenty. Slowly, the church empties out, apart from a few old women, the faithful servants. Two of them stand across from each other, folding up the white cloth that was on top of my mother. They fold it lengthwise first, and then horizontally, until it's a small square and then they slip off-screen noiselessly. Another old woman comes and picks up my flowers from their stand and bears them away, her pale blue scarf floating in the air behind her. My mother's photo sits on the stand where the flowers were, the tall pillar candle lit beside it.

The fur coat was upstairs in a wardrobe. Her eyes lit up when she saw it.

'Give it sure, for a second.' She's dressed to go to Shandon Street, white lace top from Penneys, lipstick on already.

I hand it over. 'It's vintage, be careful.'

'Go 'way out of that, sure I'm smaller than you are. What do you think?'

'It's actually nice on you.' Grudgingly. The fluffy grey fur makes her eyes look properly hazel. Her magenta hair is neatly combed over to one side, like she's making her confirmation.

'Will I stand up on the marble?'

'No, you're grand there, the light is coming in on you.'

She stands, straight-backed, in the middle of the arch between the front room and the kitchen. Puts her hands behind her back neatly, like the young girl she once was, winning medals for Irish dancing. She cocks one hip slightly, eyes crinkling, front tooth wearing a tiny little smudge of pink lipstick. 'Come on so Noelle, take a good one, aren't I lovely?'

Author's note

Not long ago, I wrote a passage about a party in Cork. I described what we did and what we said, finishing with the memory of my mother and father dancing with me and their new granddaughter across the swirly patterned floor of a hotel function room.

It was only when I watched a video of that night that I saw the hotel carpet had a geometric print, not swirly like I had said.

By then, I was nearly finished writing this book, and that geometric carpet went off like a bomb in my head. I didn't even think to question my memories until then. I had been sure it was a swirly carpet. I could see my feet moving across it. I remembered it so well.

I want to believe that my version is the objective version of events, but I have to accept – the geometric carpet forces me to accept – that I'm just one witness, doing my best to get a story straight, at a distance, over time, and in pace with an interior landscape that's constantly changing.

So, this book – while true – offers only one perspective on my mother and on my whole family, and that perspective is clouded by subjectivity, distinguished by blind spots, complicated by distance (when I first started writing about Mammy, I had lived on the other side of the world from her for more than twenty years), and – as I am continuing to discover – sometimes unreliable recall.

I know, too, that I have always had the tendency to present things in a certain way. With me in the most flattering light, mainly. The time I have spent writing about my mother has forced me to consider that I may not be the hero of my own story in the way I thought I would be. None of us are, probably.

Nor am I her only child. My brothers and sister have their own stories of our mother and we all have different Mammys; whereas I had for most of my life an antagonist, my siblings had a staunch advocate, a late-night confidante, and an irrepressible partner in crime. Mammy was the weather in our family – changeable, primal, unavoidable. There was no point arguing with her, and an interaction with her could change your day, your plans and your outlook on life in general.

This is a true story. The names and identifying details of individuals in this book have been changed in places to protect their privacy, unless otherwise requested. Some conversations have been reconstructed from memory with, as discussed, all the fallibility that entails.

Acknowledgements

I am grateful to my father, John McCarthy, my brothers John Paul and Robert, and especially to my sister Sarah for their help in remembering things I didn't know I'd forgotten. Thank you to my aunt, Cay Cooney, for sharing your memories, and to my uncle, Len Speight, who has been firing my imagination since I was very small.

At Penguin Random House New Zealand this book was in the care of a team of stellar women, all of whom made it better, led by Claire Murdoch, who took the idea from inception to final draft. Thank you, Claire, for your impeccable instincts, your steadying faith and for love hearts in the margins. Heartfelt thanks to Vanessa Manhire, structure wizard, for brilliant, deft editing and meticulous fact-checking that extended to a deep dive on Irish confectionary. Louisa Kasza, thank you for your insightful notes, your editorial expertise and nerves of steel when it came to the vagaries of international couriers. Katrina Duncan, thank you for your beautiful design. Thank you Jo Crichton for saving me from myself with your welcome logic and careful proof-reading. Thanks to Rachel Eadie for support and dumplings.

Stephen Langdon, thank you for allowing me to use the photograph on the cover. Emily Simpson, thank you for the *Sunday* shoot from whence the photo came.

Thank you, Clem Cairns and the Fish Publishing International Short Memoir Prize in West Cork, for giving me my start, and to Steve Braunias at *Newsroom* and Henry Oliver at *Metro* magazine for your support of early material, parts of which are adapted here.

With love and gratitude to Emma Espiner for Thursday emails, and for suggesting Renée; and to Renée for ten weeks of rigour and intelligent feedback that took this project from a vague idea to something that might be published.

Thank you, Mrs Breen, for *The Merchant of Venice,* public speaking competitions and telling me to reach for the stars. Thank you, Tom Dunne, for your unflagging support and many happy times with vampires. Thank you Peta Mathias, for your kindness to a stranger.

More thanks:

Edel, Ruth, Rebecca, Maddy and Lauren for decades of friendship.

Kristine Crabb – you're an inspiration, especially on the hammer days.

Bridget Healy, for the writing desk and for giving me your bed at Ballynoe.

Suzy and Janet for wise counsel and for being CCs.

Max, Morgan, Sarah, Sue, Emma McD and Lily for the SOS texts, and the lols.

Little Sez for the packets of pens – I used them all!

Meg Mason – for your support and flagrant generosity, as

placeholder for umpteen things from the dairy, please accept this acknowledgement.

To Vanessa Underwood, for believing in a turn-pager and driving lessons at Piha.

To Kirsty and Michelle, for all you do for women and for upskilling me.

Helen Forlong, for cups of tea and your kindness to me and my family.

To Lisa, Dan and the kaiako of Bell St Early Learning Centre in Featherston. You do an amazing job. This book couldn't have been written without you.

To my mother-in-law Mary, for your love and support.

To Eve, for being yourself.

Most of all, to my husband John Daniell, who not only came up with the idea for this book and its title, but who also made a million sacrifices and accommodations so I could write it. I love you. Charlie Mike.

And finally, thank you Mammy. I came out of you. I won't ever forget it.

Noelle McCarthy is an award-winning writer and broadcaster.

'Buck Rabbit', her first foray into non-fiction, won the Short Memoir section of the Fish Publishing International Writing competition in 2020.

Since 2017, she and her husband John Daniell have been making critically acclaimed podcasts as Bird of Paradise Productions.

She has written columns, reviews, first-person essays and features for a wide range of media in New Zealand, including *Metro*, the *New Zealand Herald* and *Newsroom*. In Ireland, she's provided commentary for radio and written for the *Irish Times*, the *Independent* and the *Irish Examiner*.

With nearly twenty years' experience in radio, she is a go-to host at writers' festivals and has interviewed some of the world's most famous and well-respected storytellers, from Eleanor Catton to Marlon James, Margaret Atwood and James Cameron.

She lives in the New Zealand countryside with her husband and their daughter, and she misses Irish chocolate.